Management for New GPs

RCGP Curriculum for
General Practice Series

# Management for New GPs

*Edited by Veronica Wilkie and Peter Spurgeon*

The Royal College of General Practitioners was founded in 1952 with this object:

*'To encourage, foster and maintain the highest possible standards in general practice and for that purpose to take or join with others in taking steps consistent with the charitable nature of that object which may assist towards the same.'*

Among its responsibilities under its Royal Charter the College is entitled to:

*'Diffuse information on all matters affecting general practice and issue such publications as may assist the object of the College.'*

British Library Cataloguing-in-Publication Data
A catalogue record for this book is available from the British Library


Published by the Royal College of General Practitioners 2008
14 Princes Gate, Hyde Park, London SW7 1PU



**Disclaimer**
This publication is intended for the use of medical practitioners in the UK and not for patients. The authors, editors and publisher have taken care to ensure that the information contained in this book is correct to the best of their knowledge, at the time of publication. Whilst efforts have been made to ensure the accuracy of the information presented, particularly that related to the prescription of drugs, the authors, editors and publisher cannot accept liability for information that is subsequently shown to be wrong. Readers are advised to check that the information, especially that related to drug usage, complies with information contained in the *British National Formulary*, or equivalent, or manufacturers' datasheets, and that it complies with the latest legislation and standards of practice.

Designed and typeset by the Typographic Design Unit
Printed by Hobbs the Printers Ltd
Indexed by Carol Ball

ISBN: 978-0-85084-319-4

# Contents

List of contributors *vii*
Preface *x*
List of abbreviations *xi*

**Chapter 1** | *Veronica Wilkie*
History of general practice 1

**Chapter 2** | *Peter Spurgeon*
The interface between general practice and the wider NHS 15

**Chapter 3** | *Juliet Woodin and Elizabeth Wade*
Commissioning and contracting 23

**Chapter 4** | *Veronica Wilkie*
Managing performance in general practice: the role of clinical governance, the National Patient Safety Authority, National Clinical Assessment Service and revalidation 39

**Chapter 5** | *Jim Waits*
The primary healthcare team 59

**Chapter 6** | *Richard Lambert*
The GP running a business: what you need to know from your accountant 79

**Chapter 7** | *Jim Waits*
The GP practice as an employer 107

**Chapter 8** | *Hugh Flanagan*
Motivating and developing the team 123

**Chapter 9** | *Robert Cragg*
Organising and running a meeting 139

**Chapter 10** | *Peter Spurgeon*
The GP as a leader 151

**Chapter 11** | *Robert Cragg*
Time management 161

**Chapter 12** | *Jag Dhaliwal*
Motivating the individual 171

**Chapter 13** | *Veronica Wilkie*
Change management: putting evidence into practice 183

**Chapter 14** | *Robert Cragg and Veronica Wilkie*
Developing a business case 193

**Chapter 15** | *Jonathan Howes*
Project management 203

Index 221

# Contributors

**Dr Veronica Wilkie** MBChB MSc FRCGP DCH DGM DOccMed DPD DRCOG is a GP in Droitwich, Worcestershire, and a Senior Clinical Teaching Fellow at the Institute of Clinical Leadership, Warwick Medical School. She has been a GP tutor, GP trainer and undergraduate tutor before moving to her current post at Warwick Medical School. She currently divides her time between clinical practice and teaching healthcare leadership and management to doctors in training, and is a medical adviser to the NHS Institute's Enhancing Engagement in Medical Leadership project. She is also the Curriculum Guardian for RCGP statement 3.5 *Evidence-Based Practice.*

**Prof. Peter Spurgeon** BSc PhD ABPS is Professor of Health Service Management and Director at the Institute of Clinical Leadership, at the University of Warwick's Medical School. Peter has worked in a number of universities, both in the UK and overseas, as well as in the private sector. Previously he was Director of the Health Services Management Centre (HSMC) at the University of Birmingham and holds honorary chairs in Australia and Italy. He has a particular interest in clinical leadership and in supporting the transition of practitioners into leadership roles. Currently he is seconded to the NHS Institute for Innovation and Improvement, where he is the Project Director on the national Enhancing Engagement in Medical Leadership project, with the Academy of Medical Royal Colleges.



**Robert Cragg** BSc MSc works jointly as both a Senior Research Associate for the Institute of Clinical Leadership at the University of Warwick and as Leadership Development Manager for NHS West Midlands. His career includes managerial experience within both primary and secondary care, in both project and operational management positions. Currently Robert is studying towards a doctorate, examining the role of clinical directors in the NHS and organisational development strategies that can be deployed to support such positions, in the interest of enhanced job satisfaction and managerial efficiency. This current role has enabled him to specialise in the commissioning and evaluation of region-wide leadership programmes.

**Dr Jag Dhaliwal** MBChB MSc FRCGP is a general practitioner in Walsall. He is Honorary Associate Professor and Director of the Masters in Health Services Management Programme at the University of Warwick. Jag obtained an MSc in Health Care Management with Distinction in 2001 from Warwick for his dissertation looking at the performance management of doctors. He has worked in public health and NHS management, holding the roles of Director of Primary Care Development and Interim Medical Director. He has extensive experience as a coach and mentor with a particular interest and expertise in the unique opportunities and stresses encountered by clinicians in leadership roles. As Director of the NHS/RCGP Midland Faculty Leadership Programme since January 2008, Jag has been responsible for designing and leading this broad, multidisciplinary and region-wide course, which aims to boost participants' effectiveness in enhancing service quality. Jag has lectured in the UK, South America and Asia, and he is also course director of a highly evaluated Spanish language leadership programme for Latin American health service professionals based at the University of Warwick.

**Hugh Flanagan MSocSc MHSM ChMCIPD DipHSM** is Managing Director of the Organisational Research and Consultancy Network (International) Limited (ORCNI) and works closely with the Institute of Clinical Leadership at the University of Warwick. He has held positions with the NHS, the University of Birmingham and in the private sector. Specialising in leadership and organisational behaviour and development, he has undertaken a number of research projects. This includes a significant project with particular reference to the NHS, published as *Public Sector Managerial Effectiveness* (with Prof. Peter Spurgeon; Open University Press, 1996). Hugh has written about leadership and organisational development in health and public sector organisations, and has lectured at postgraduate level and carried out senior management training on these topics worldwide. He currently works on leadership and management development programmes for doctors in primary and secondary care, as well as for professionals and managers in other areas. Hugh's other current areas of research are quality improvement, identifying the causes of organisational stress and poor performance, and the design and delivery of individual, team and organisational learning processes.



**Jonathan Howes BA (Hons)** is a PRINCE2 practitioner and is currently a project manager at NHS West Midlands Strategic Health Authority, working within the workforce deanery. Jonathan has worked as a project manager in both the public and private sectors, specialising in the introduction of information technology.

**Richard Lambert** is a chartered accountant who has spent the last 20 years acting for doctors, from GP locums at the start of their careers to principals in practice approaching retirement. Richard set up his own Midlands-based accountancy practice, Lambert & Co, in 1991 with the express purpose of providing the full range of specialist services required by doctors. Richard has considerable experience in guiding practices through periods of expansion and partnership changes, including cash flow forecasting both for new surgery builds and financing retiring partners, and more recently advising practices in general, and dispensing practices in particular, following changes to the VAT status of medical services. Richard has also advised doctors following the recent and extensive changes to the NHS superannuation scheme, which has had a significant impact on both locums' and principals' pension provisions, as well as considering the cash flow and taxation implications arising.

**Elizabeth Wade** **BA MSc PGCert** is a Senior Fellow in the Health Services Management Centre (HSMC) at the University of Birmingham, where she leads the centre's work on health and social care commissioning. This involves co-directing the university's MSc in Public Service Commissioning, and coordinating the department's research and consultancy activities in this field. Before joining HSMC in December 2005, Elizabeth was the Head of Primary Care Commissioning for a Primary Care Trust (PCT) in London, where she was responsible for leading the commissioning of all primary medical, dental, pharmacy and community health services, and for integrating the commissioning of primary care services within the PCT's overarching service development strategy. Prior to this, Elizabeth performed a number of other commissioning, primary care development and project management roles within Primary Care Groups (PCGs) and PCTs, following completion of the NHS Graduate Management Training Scheme. In several of her previous roles Elizabeth has been responsible for planning, managing and commissioning diabetes services. As a result, she has a particular interest in the role of primary healthcare teams in the management of long-term conditions.

**Jim Waits** **IPFA** is the practice manager at St Johns House surgery in Worcester. He has held various senior positions in the NHS including Chief Executive of Worcester and District Health Authority, 1985–96. He was a member of the Steering Group for the BMA's 'Advance Statements about Medical Treatment' and a member of the General Medical Council, 1996–7.

**Juliet Woodin** **BA MPhil PhD MIHM** is a Senior Fellow at the Health Services Management Centre, University of Birmingham. She has, since 1984, held various management positions in the NHS and was Chief Executive of Nottingham Health Authority, 1996–2002. Before that she was a lecturer and researcher in public policy and public administration. Her current academic interests include health policy, commissioning, and leadership and management development.

# Preface

This book is an introduction to leadership and management, intended for GP registrars and GPs with newly appointed management roles. The book is not intended to be a complete and exhaustive reference to what is an increasingly large subject area with a burgeoning number of university masters degrees and professional qualifications. We hope that it will be a practical guide and reference tool.

When thinking about what should be included in this book we were first guided by the RCGP's curriculum for specialty training for general practice, using the curriculum statements *Management in Primary Care* and *Evidence-Based Practice* as guides. We also asked practising GPs what we should cover and received a wide range of responses, from requests for what the structure and function of the NHS were (largely from doctors very new to general practice), to how to run a practice (from newly appointed GPs in practice) to how to be a leader and manage 'oneself' (from more established GPs). We have therefore divided the book into three sections, starting with a description of the NHS and the role of general practice and the primary care organisations, and how current management processes (Practice-Based Commissioning) are designed. The middle part of the book concentrates more on practice-based organisation and management. The final part looks at the individual skills and aptitudes needed by the GP as a manager and leader.

We are well aware of the fact that certain aspects of this book might become out of date, as quickly as a major change in leadership of the Department of Health occurs, and that Chapter 3 ('Commissioning and contracting') might become an annexe to Chapter 1 ('History of general practice') and might have to be rewritten with every successive edition.

Our authors come from a variety of backgrounds: working general practitioners; a practice manager; practice accountants; and professionals experienced in a broad base of healthcare management backgrounds. We hope they have provided a practical and informative background to their individual subjects.

Dr Veronica Wilkie
Professor Peter Spurgeon
December 2008

# List of abbreviations

| | |
|---|---|
| ACAS | Advisory, Conciliation and Arbitration Service |
| AKT | Applied Knowledge Test |
| APMS | Alternative Provider Medical Services |
| BMA | British Medical Association |
| BMJ | *British Medical Journal* |
| CHP | Community Health Partnership |
| CPD | Continuing Professional Development |
| CSA | Clinical Skills Assessment |
| DDA | Disability Discrimination Act |
| DENs | Doctor's Educational Needs |
| DES | Direct Enhanced Services |
| DHSSPS | Department of Health, Social Services and Public Safety |
| DoH | Department of Health |
| EBM | Evidence-Based Medicine |
| EBP | Evidence-Based Practice |
| FHSA | Family Health Service Authority |
| FY2 | Foundation Year 2 |
| GMC | General Medical Council |
| GMS | General Medical Services |
| GPC | General Practitioners Committee |
| GPFH | General Practice Fundholder |
| GPwSI | GP with a Special Interest |
| HCA | healthcare assistant |
| HCHS | hospital and community health services |
| HMRC | HM Revenue and Customs |
| HSMC | Health Services Management Centre |
| LCG | local commissioning group |
| LES | Local Enhanced Services |
| LHB | Local Health Board |
| LIFT | Local Improvement Finance Trusts |
| LMC | Local Medical Committee |
| MDU | Medical Defence Union |
| MPS | Medical Protection Society |
| NCAS | National Clinical Assessment Authority |
| NI | National Insurance |
| NICE | National Institute for Health and Clinical Excellence |
| NPSA | National Patient Safety Authority |

| | |
|---|---|
| NSF | National Service Frameworks |
| OT | occupational therapist |
| PBC | Practice-Based Commissioning |
| PCG | Primary Care Group |
| PCO | Primary Care Organisation |
| PCT | Primary Care Trust |
| PCTMS | Primary Care Trust Medical Services |
| PDP | Practice Development Plan |
| PEC | Professional Executive Committee |
| PFI | Private Finance Initiative |
| PGEA | Postgraduate Education Allowance |
| PHCT | primary healthcare team |
| PID | Project Initiation Document |
| PMETB | Postgraduate Medical Education and Training Board |
| PMS | Personal Medical Services |
| PREP | Post-Registration Education and Practice |
| PSI | Patient Safety Incident |
| PUNs | Patient's Unmet Needs |
| QoF | Quality and Outcomes Framework |
| RCGP | Royal College of General Practitioners |
| SHA | Strategic Health Authority |
| VTS | Vocational Training Scheme |
| WPBA | Workplace-Based Assessment |

# History of general practice

# 1

*Veronica Wilkie*

***Scenario***

*You have nearly reached the end of your registrar year and there has been a complaint by one of your patients, whose elderly mother recently had required several visits following a fall. She is concerned that there has been a lack of continuity and that her elderly mother is confused as to what she can do. You look through the notes and see that out of six visits she has had three different doctors out to see her, two as urgent calls, the rest as planned visits. You were the last one to go. You arrange to go and visit her at the same time as her daughter. Whilst you are discussing the issues that led to the complaint, the elderly woman remarks that 'It's not the same. Not so long ago there was only one doctor and you could be sure that he would always come and see you.' At coffee you ask the other doctors how general practice has changed.*



## Introduction

General practice has always been described as the 'jewel in the crown' of the health service in the NHS, in a country that prides itself on being able to treat any of its citizens regardless of the ability to pay. Most GPs now work in practices and alongside other healthcare practitioners, and increasingly deal with chronic diseases as a greater proportion of their healthcare consultations than their colleagues did 50 years ago. Modern-day general practice has evolved from care provided by apothecaries (alongside physicians and surgeons) in the early nineteenth century to care provided by a team of individuals, the doctors having now to not only achieve a certified level of competency, but also, from 2007, to pass the membership examination of the Royal College of General Practitioners (RCGP), bringing the entrance onto the generalist register of the General Medical Council (GMC) in line with the specialist colleges. GPs have evolved a service initially by slow evolution, more latterly much more quickly because of calls for 'reform' and to continue the 'pace of change' by the politicians. Kenneth Calman described the purpose of medicine as:

*to serve the community by continually improving health, healthcare and the quality of life for the individual and the population by health promotion, prevention of illness, treatment and care and the effective use of resources.*[1]

This chapter looks to review the history of general practice and how it has reached its current place in the modern-day NHS. It discusses some of the key legislation and reforms that have built modern-day general practice and its unique place in primary care in the developed world.

Box 1.1 lists some facts about general practice.

Box 1.1 ○ ***Consultation figures for UK general practice***

- In 2003 there were 260 million consultations between patients and GPs every year (this excludes practice-nurse consultations, which are thought to be about 100 million).
- The national average consultation rate is four consultations with a GP per person per year, rising to seven per year for adults over 75.
- 15 per cent of the entire population sees a GP in any two-week period.
- Each full-time GP will complete between 7000 and 8000 consultations a year.
- General practice is responsible for 51 per cent of all contacts in the NHS, primary care as a whole for 80 per cent (this includes NHS Direct, walk-in centres, dental treatment and community staff contacts).
- Secondary care sees 18 per cent of all contacts, with outpatient attendances accounting for 7 per cent and emergency inpatient 6 per cent.

*Source*: RCGP.[2]



## The development of general practice, from ancient civilisations to the nineteenth century

Medicine had already gone through several stages of transformation by the nineteenth century. There is archaeological evidence of 'physicians' from 1500 BC in ancient Egypt. One such example was the Egyptian physician Irj whose tombstone described him as:

*palace doctor, superintendent of the court physicians, palace eye physician, palace physician of the belly and one who understands the internal fluids and who is guardian of the anus.*

This is a reasonable description of a generalist, albeit one with rather select patients. By the time of Hippocrates in ancient Greece, medicine and its practitioners had started to develop an intellectual and scientific discipline. Archaeologists and historians had found evidence of a training system via an apprenticeship, with the practitioners, often from an aristocratic background, consulting out of 'offices', often in the vicinity of a temple and charging a fee for each service.[3]

Throughout the Dark Ages, the practice of healing in Britain was closely associated with the church, and was highly institutionalised. Most monasteries had a herb garden and used herbs to treat illnesses, with 'infirmaries' to house the sick an essential part of each monastery. In the Middle Ages physicians had started to become separated from the monasteries, but were very few in number. These 'doctors' were often of high rank and had academic connections. They spent more time thinking about disease in philosophical terms than providing care.[4]

By the seventeenth century physicians (who had formed the Royal College of Physicians in the sixteenth century) were only available to those wealthy few who could afford to pay. Apothecaries had dissociated themselves from grocers, and had formed their own society. Initially they were restricted to filling out prescriptions and 'bleeding' individuals, but increasingly began to treat the patients, most of whom came from households who were not able to pay for physicians. At the end of the seventeenth century a bitter battle raged over the right of apothecaries to treat patients, Apothecaries started to metamorphose into general practitioners in 1704 after a particularly long legal battle about payment for services. Surgeons did not separate from barbers until 1745, forming the Royal College of Surgeons by royal charter in 1799.

The British Medical Association (BMA) Medical Reform Committee successfully secured the passing of the 1858 Medical Act after 20 years of negotiation. The act established the GMC and the Medical Register, therefore distinguishing, for the first time, between qualified and unqualified practitioners. Important amendment acts were later passed, including the 1886 Medical Act, after which it became mandatory for all practitioners to qualify in medicine, surgery and midwifery rather than in any one of these areas. The 1886 act also enabled the profession to directly elect representatives onto the council of the GMC.[5]

Throughout the eighteenth and nineteenth centuries apothecaries started to provide services in the community and became more accepted as general practitioners of medicine.[6]

## The twentieth century

At the start of the twentieth century GPs were mostly practising as single-handed practitioners, from their own homes, and – as they were almost always men – their wives provided unpaid reception work. These doctors were on call 24 hours a day, seven days a week, and worked alongside district nurses whom the local authorities employed. By this time GPs were graduating from medical schools but were thought to have all the skills necessary to practise family medicine on leaving medical school, and were certainly thought to have the knowledge and skills to take them to retirement. The only employed staff tended to be dispensers, with the doctor and/or his wife doing the practice accounts.

In 1919 David Lloyd George led the National Health Insurance Act, which for the first time initiated registration with a GP, but only for working men who earned less than £250 per year. The act also allowed for some financial reimbursement or payment of their treatment. The doctors who participated in the 'panel' scheme gave their services to these men for free. Their dependants and those who fell outside the bands were still seen as private patients.

Figure 1.1 ○ ***First council meeting of the College of General Practitioners***

Plans to provide a National Health Service were debated and developed throughout the 1920s and 1930s, before being interrupted by the Second World War. Despite the overwhelming nature of the war for the government, William Beveridge still put together a report in 1942 about providing a Welfare State, with the Health Service being central to its care. Following this the National Health Act was passed in 1946. This led to free access to general medical services, and GPs were paid by a capitation-based system, embedding their role as gatekeepers to specialist care, a role that is thought to have led to the relatively lower cost of health care than the systems allowing direct access to specialists.[7] Nye Bevan also brought to the fore the need for better public health.

Writing in 1952, he said:

> *The preventive health services of modern society fight the battle over a wider front and therefore less dramatically than is the case with personal medicine. Yet the victories won by preventive medicine are much the most important for mankind. This is not so only because it is obviously preferable to prevent suffering rather than alleviate it. Preventive medicine, which is merely another way of saying collective action, builds up a system of social habits that constitute an indispensable part of what we mean by civilisation.*



What of GPs as a profession? The first and unsuccessful attempt at providing GPs with their own college was in 1845. A century later GPs were in danger of being isolated as the National Health Service was formed; they had little academic leadership of their own and very little influence over undergraduate and postgraduate teaching. A letter in the *British Medical Journal* (BMJ) in 1951 said:

> *There is a College of Physicians, a College of Surgeons, a College of Obstetricians and Gynaecologists, a College of Nursing, a College of Midwives, and a College of Veterinary Surgeons, all of them Royal Colleges; there is a College of Speech Therapists and a College of Physical Education: but there is no college or academic body to represent primarily the interests of the largest group of medical personnel in this country – the 20,000 general practitioners.*[8]

The College of General Practitioners was founded in 1952, achieving its royal charter in 1967, 300 years after the formation of the Royal College of Physicians.

In 1950 *The Lancet* published a piece of work that shook the establishment. The author, J S Collings, an Australian, had worked as a GP in New Zealand and Canada before becoming a research fellow at Harvard University. His work is an ethnographic study of general practice, recording his observations after sitting in at 55 practices for four or five days. His analysis of the plight of the GP was probably correct, that they were marginalised, excluded from hospitals and had a declining status.[9] Scrutiny of the paper since its publication has led to major doubts about the research validity, and letters in the BMJ after publication suggested that generalisation beyond the practices sampled was 'both unscientific and unjustified'.[10]

He stated that 'some (working conditions) are bad enough to require con demnation in the public interest'. He called rural practice an 'anachronism', suburban practice a 'casualty-clearing' service, and that inner-city practice was 'at best ... very unsatisfactory and at worst a positive source of public danger'.

The Collings report was acclaimed 'a classic report' and 'the most devastating attack on the family doctor', and was a seminal contribution to the formation of the College of General Practitioners.[8] Despite its methodological weaknesses it was still successful in mobilising a change in general practice and to the development of group practices, with the development of a 'new' contract for GPs, the 'GP Charter' in the 1960s.

In the mid-1960s the 'GP Charter' had a significant effect on how general practice was delivered. For the first time provision was made for premises, paying for groups of GPs and other members of the primary healthcare team to be housed under one roof. GPs increasingly frequently began to work in groups and there was a rapid increase in the number of health centres. Health visitors first started to be 'attached' to groups of GPs, followed by district nurses, at first on an experimental basis, then more formally after the Health Service and Public Health Act of 1968. During the 1970s practice nurses started to work in practices, only achieving a 'pensionable' status within the NHS in the 1990s.

In the 1960s a few practices and districts had GP trainees, who were attached to a practice in order to learn their profession before becoming independent practitioners. However, it was not until 1981, with the Vocational Training Act of 1977, that vocational training became mandatory, with the initial requirement of all GPs spending one year as a 'trainee' in a recognised training practice. This was quickly followed by a requirement for three years post-full registration training in approved posts from 1982. Throughout the 1980s the increasing complexity and rapid pace of change in technology led to the increasing need for good administration and management in the NHS. Some key reports leading to the current professional management of the health service were:

- **1983** ○ the Griffiths report, which looked at the general management of hospital and community services
- **1985** ○ the RCGP's *Quality in General Practice* policy statement
- **1986** ○ the green paper *Primary Health Care: an agenda for discussion*

- **1987** ○ the white paper *Promoting Better Health*, in which Family Practitioner Committees were given a more clear managerial role
- **1989** ○ the white paper *Working for Patients*, which led to the NHS and Community Care Act 1990, and started the British healthcare revolution that was the internal market.

---

## General Medical Services, the internal market and fundholding

In 1990 GPs were given a new contract, which enabled GPs to be more directly accountable for the costs of providing health care and introduced targets that attracted payments (immunisation) and initially provided increased payment through the provision of health promotion clinics. GPs for the first time were expected to attend meetings for postgraduate training and were remunerated via a 'Postgraduate Education Allowance' (PGEA) for 30 hours of attendance at lectures and meetings. Prior to this CPD (Continuing Professional Development) had been done as a 'voluntary' activity. General practices also were inspected by Family Health Service Authorities (FHSAs), who were made more responsible for the provision of care.

- The internal market separated purchasers from providers of health care. Costs of procedures and episodes of health care were drawn up, with a view to driving up the efficiency and accountability of the healthcare professions and providers. GPs were able to hold budgets based on their patients' needs, starting with larger practices at first and ending with amalgamated purchasing groups of smaller practices after five or six years. General practices had to become increasingly businesslike, practice managers were becoming increasingly vital, had better developed training and often worked alongside business or 'fund' managers. The NHS moved with other aspects of public sector management ascribed by some as the paradigm of 'New Public Management', which comprises a move to using principles of private sector 'business management' in the public sector. This placed the responsibility for organisational policy, success and efficiency on the managers.[11]

However, there was public perception and political anxiety about fundholding causing a two-tier service, with fundholding practices obtaining better 'deals' and waits for their patients than non-GP fundholders. This led to a rethink by the Labour government in 1997. The white paper *The New NHS: modern, dependable* sought to deliver health care in a 'third way' based on partnership driven by performance. It had six key principles:

- ▷ to renew the NHS as a genuinely national service, offering fair access to consistently high-quality, prompt and accessible services right across the country
- ▷ to make the delivery of health care against these new national standards a matter of local responsibility, with local doctors and nurses in the driving seat in shaping services
- ▷ to get the NHS to work in partnership, breaking down organisational barriers and forging stronger links with local authorities
- ▷ to drive efficiency through a more rigorous approach to performance, cutting bureaucracy to maximise every pound spent in the NHS for the care of patients
- ▷ to shift the focus onto quality of care so that excellence would be guaranteed to all patients, with quality the driving force for decision-making at every level of the service
- ▷ to rebuild public confidence in the NHS as a public service, accountable to patients, open to the public and shaped by their views.[12]



Its aim was to replace the internal market by integrated care. The white paper described a programme of 10-year evolution of change rather than organisational upheaval.[12]

---

### Personal Medical Services

In 1998 general practices were offered an alternative to the General Medical Services (GMS) contract that they signed up to in 1991. Personal Medical Services (or PMS) was developed initially as a pilot to reflect the problems the older contract had in its lack of flexibility around provision of services, and how GPs were employed. The changing demographics and increasing flexibility in employment practices throughout the NHS meant that many more GPs were women who had family commitments and who did not want to contract to 24 hour responsibility and out-of-hours care. The changing nature of management of health problems in primary care meant that more flexibility of multiprofessional working was needed. The PMS contract allowed GPs to employ other GPs, and to have their income determined according to clinical contracts at the beginning of the year, with greater flexibility to employ staff within that budget. Primary Care Trusts (PCTs) were also able to look at the local needs and work with practices to:

- ▷ encourage a greater skill mix and team-based approach
- ▷ address recruitment problems
- ▷ tackle under-doctored areas in new and innovative ways.

By 2004, when the 'pilot' ended, the Department of Health estimated that 40 per cent of practices were PMS rather than GMS.[13]

---

## The GMS2 contract

This contract was negotiated by the Department of Health in 2003. It covered existing GMS practices but also was extended so that PMS contracts were altered to allow for the newer ways of working. Its essence was said to be that it allowed a 'new' way of working, and reflected the problems in GP recruitment because of the ongoing problem of providing out-of-hours care. It was also designed to allow greater flexibility, for GPs to provide a 'core' element of services and then to opt in or out of 'additional services' and to be commissioned and paid extra for providing enhanced services as agreed with the PCT, according to local need. Its most powerful change was that GPs were able to opt out of out-of-hours care and were contracted as a baseline to provide essential services between 8.00 a.m. and 6.30 p.m. It was hailed as a way of providing greater flexibility in the provision of services, in a way that was more sensitive to local need. It would reward good clinical practice financially, and facilitate the modernisation of premises and IT, giving ever greater responsibility to contracting PCTs to develop services. Each GMS and PMS (although the rewards are calculated to take into account some of the provision in the PMS budget) practice was able to work towards the Quality and Outcomes Framework (QoF) (see Table 1.1, p. 10) in three domains (1050 points in all) as well as being paid extra for providing additional or enhanced services.

Significantly the new contract was between a practice and the Primary Care Organisation (PCTs or Primary Care Groups [PCGs] in England and Health Boards in Scotland and Northern Ireland) and not an individual doctor, and patients were no longer registered with one doctor but with a practice. There was a significant shift in the Department of Health in terms of access to health care, stating a healthcare professional instead of 'your doctor', thus allowing further freedom in healthcare provision and further distance between the age-old expectation of a single family doctor who provided all of a patient's primary care.

The 'nGMS' contract described practice activity as being for:

### *Essential (core) services*

- ▷ Management of patients who are ill or believe themselves to be ill, with conditions from which recovery is generally expected, for the duration

Table 1.1 ○ ***The original and updated domains for the Quality and Outcomes Framework***[14]

***QoF points***

| **Clinical standards** | **Patient experience** |
|---|---|
| • CHD<br>• Stroke<br>• Hypertension<br>• Diabetes<br>• COPD<br>• Epilepsy<br>• Mental Health<br>• Hypothyroidism<br>• Asthma | Completion of questionnaires and action on them |
| **Organisational standards** | **Revisions 2006/07** |
| • Records and Information<br>• Education and Training<br>• Practice Management<br>• Medicines Management | Clinical standards; atrial fibrillation, heart failure, depression, dementia, chronic kidney disease, obesity, learning disability |

of that condition. This includes health promotion advice and referral as appropriate, reflecting patient choice where practicable.

- ▷ General management of patients who are terminally ill.
- ▷ The management of chronic disease in the manner determined by the practice in discussion with the patient.[15]
- ▷ To provide care in the home where appropriate.

### *Additional services*

These are services for which practices could opt out and the PCT could look for an alternative provider, but in doing so the practice would 'lose' that funding:

- ▷ cervical screening
- ▷ contraceptive services
- ▷ vaccinations and immunisations
- ▷ child health surveillance
- ▷ maternity services
- ▷ minor surgery services.

### *Enhanced services*

These are either agreed nationally (Direct Enhanced Services [DES]) or locally according to local population need (Local Enhanced Services [LES]). The services are thought to be essential or additional services delivered to a higher standard, and might include services for substance abuse, enhanced minor surgery services, or provision of a GP with a special interest in other clinical specialties.

In 2006, for a multitude of reasons, not least because GPs had consistently outperformed the Department of Health's expectations, 166 of the points were recycled, 138 to new clinical areas, 28 to existing areas. Points initially earmarked to be given for patient access were 'moved' to allow for other clinical domains to be performance managed. The total number of points available remained unchanged at 1050. Other 'enhanced services' were altered to improved access and patient experience. Small funds were made available for practices booking patients through the electronic 'Choose and Book' service.



---

## Alternative Provider Medical Services

In 2004 there was a further amendment to the National Health Service Act 1977, allowing for 'Alternative Provider Medical Services' (APMS). This change allowed for organisations outside the NHS and 'traditional general practice' to provide medical services and contract with PCTs. It was brought in so that services could be obtained in areas of under-provision, or for provision of additional services where practices had opted out, and to improve access in areas where there were problems with GP recruitment and retention. The APMS provider could be existing commercial or voluntary public bodies, GMS (and PMS) practices or NHS and NHS foundation trusts. The contract for these services and the exact nature and standards of care are determined by the local contracting PCT.[15]

---

## Primary Care Trust Medical Services

Primary Care Trust Medical Services (PCTMS), in another amendment, allow PCTs to employ and provide medical services again where GMS/PMS practices have opted out or there are specified local reasons for doing so, or there is under-provision of services.[16]

## Practice-Based Commissioning

This currently is the way in which health services are commissioned and is covered in greater detail in Chapter 3.

## Modernising Medical Careers – training new general practitioners

Modernising Medical Careers arose out of a need to look afresh at the way all doctors are trained, and one of many aims was to ensure that all medical specialties had a recognised exit point from training. From 2007, all GPs will have to pass a series of competency tests and will all take the nMRCGP examination. Before 2007, membership of the RCGP was voluntary, GPs in training having had to pass a summative assessment of competencies for several years if they chose not to take the 'old' membership examination, MRCGP. For the first time access to the GMC register for general practice will be dependent on successful completion of an integrated programme that includes an Applied Knowledge Test (AKT), Clinical Skills Assessment (CSA) and Workplace-Based Assessment (WPBA). This brings doctors who are general practitioners in line with their specialist colleagues who have needed to pass their colleges' membership examinations for many years.



## Conclusion

General practice has evolved from advice from an apothecary who was available to those who could not afford a physician, to a doctor working in a system where patients are seen by a number of healthcare professionals employed by a number of contractual means. The most rapid evolution has been over the last decade, where changes in contractual obligations and demographics of the GPs themselves have led to greater part-time working, more flexibility in working, provision of night and out-of-hours care by a completely different organisation from the local general practice, and patients being seen by a number of healthcare professionals in primary care. It is unsurprising therefore that the prized continuity of care as mentioned in the scenario has altered.

## Questions

1 ▷ Who provided the earliest form of community healthcare advice?

2 ▷ At the start of the twentieth century what did a typical general practice look like?

3 ▷ Who employed the district nurses at that time?

4 ▷ When was the NHS first mooted?

5 ▷ How did the panel system work?

6 ▷ What did the NHS mean for the provision of general practice?

7 ▷ What charter led to the development of health centres?

8 ▷ When did vocational training become mandatory?

9 ▷ What paper led to the development of the internal market?

10 ▷ What was the CPD provision for GPs in the 1990 contract?

11 ▷ What are PMS practices? APMS and PCTMS contracts?

12 ▷ What changes did the GMS2 contract bring to general practice?



### References

1 • Calman K. *The Profession of Medicine* London: DoH, 1994.

2 • Royal College of General Practitioners. *The Value of General Practice* [RCGP Fact Sheet] London: RCGP, 2006, www.rcgp.org.uk/pdf/ISS_INFO_06_ValueGenPrac.pdf [accessed September 2008].

3 • Lyons A, Petrucelli RJ II. Medicine in Hippocratic times. In: *Medicine: an illustrated history* New York: Abradale Press, 1987, p. 196.

4 • Lyons A, Petrucelli RJ II. The Middle Ages. In: *Medicine: an illustrated history* New York: Abradale Press, 1987, p. 338.

5 • British Medical Association. *An Outline History of the British Medical Association,* www.bma.org.uk/ap.nsf/Content/BMAOutlineHistory [accessed September 2008].

6 • Lyons A, Petrucelli RJ II. The eighteenth century. In: *Medicine: an illustrated history* New York: Abradale Press, 1987, p. 489.

7 • Coulter A. *Managing Demand: managing demand at the interface between primary and secondary care* London: King's Fund, 1998.

8 • Hunt JH. Events leading up to the formation of the steering committee. In: J Fry, Lord Hunt of Fawley, RJFH Pinsent (eds). *A History of the Royal College of General Practitioners* London: MTP Press Ltd, 1983, p. 7.

9 • Petchey R. Collings report on general practice in England in 1950: unrecognised, pioneering piece of British social research? *British Medical Journal* 1995; **311**: 40–2.

10 • Anonymous. The GP at the crossroads [editorial] *British Medical Journal* 1950; **i**: 709–13.

11 • Farnham D, Horton S. Managing public and private organisations. In: S Horton, D Farnham (eds). *Public Management in Britain* London: Macmillan, 1999, p.44.

12 • Department of Health. *The New NHS: modern, dependable: executive summary* London: DoH, 1997, www.dh.gov.uk/en/Publicationsandstatistics/Publications/PublicationsPolicyAndGuidance/DH_4010326 [accessed September 2008].

13 • Department of Health. *Sustaining Innovation through New PMS Arrangements*, 2003, www.dh.gov.uk/assetRoot/04/07/80/39/04078039.pdf [accessed September 2008].

14 • Department of Health. *Investing in General Practice: the new General Medical Services contract*, 2003, www.dh.gov.uk/assetRoot/04/07/86/58/04078658.pdf [accessed September 2008].

15 • Department of Health. *National Health Service Act 1977: Alternative Provider Medical Services directions 2004*, www.dh.gov.uk/assetRoot/04/08/02/69/04080269.pdf [accessed September 2008].

16 • Department of Health. *National Health Service Act 1977: Primary Care Trust Medical Services directions 2006*, www.dh.gov.uk/en/Publicationsandstatistics/Publications/PublicationsLegislation/DH_4137265 [accessed September 2008].

# The interface between general practice and the wider NHS

# 2

*Peter Spurgeon*

## *Scenario*

*The family were devastated when Jane, their mother, had been diagnosed with a dementing illness in her late 60s. Researching the internet, Jane's daughter had found a new and 'promising drug' for the condition. However, when the family came to see her GP they were told that the drug was very expensive and unproven, and the local Primary Care Trust (PCT) had stated that the GPs should not prescribe it. The family were surprised that the GP couldn't just 'write a prescription', and indeed wondered what the relationship was between the GP and the NHS. The GP had been forewarned of the consultation by a letter, and had been able get some more information from the pharmaceutical adviser at the PCT, understanding that the drug was unproven, and relatively untested. He also was aware that the family had relatively little information as to the structure of the NHS.*



## Introduction

For many years general practice in the UK has had an 'undifferentiated' feel to it. Patients tended to relate to their own particular doctor, historically a single-handed practitioner, more latterly a doctor with whom they were registered or had developed a good relationship. For many the doctor was seen as the person who delivered care and referred on, but was not necessarily perceived by the public as being part of a wider organisation. The contractual (rather than employed) nature of each GP also tended to strengthen this view within GPs themselves. However, as various governments have sought to introduce reforms to the NHS so primary care and general practice have been subject to increasing integration with the bodies that they contract with, in terms of funding arrangements, nominal drug budgets, and more recently Practice-Based Commissioning and the GMS2 contract. Since the 1990s an increasingly 'centralist' approach by the NHS has seen the establishment of targets and performance standards. In addition high-profile failures in healthcare provision coupled with an increasing consumerist movement have seen rising expectations about what general practice should provide and how it should operate. Most recently boundaries between primary and secondary care have been challenged by the advent of care pathways, and a current political drive to increase the range of providers, especially the private sector, and hence challenge the traditional patterns of provision of care.

Despite these changes general practice still operates in a unique environment within the NHS and this chapter will explore this in relation, in particular, to the Primary Care Organisation (PCO) and its interface with the wider NHS. It is also important to note that as devolution has advanced politically so the functioning of general practice and primary care overall has diverged more and more, with Scotland, Northern Ireland and Wales having increasingly different systems. The key aspects of these differences will be highlighted but the initial section will focus on the English context.



## The establishment of Primary Care Trusts/Organisations

Primary care represents a major component of all healthcare provision in the NHS in England. It employs 107,000 practice staff, accounting for some three quarters of total NHS funding, and 72 per cent of all contacts with the NHS are with primary care services.

The framework for the management of this aspect of the service along with the rest of the NHS was established through the government paper *Shifting the Balance of Power within the NHS* (2001), which saw the creation of *Strategic Health Authorities* (SHA) and *Primary Care Trusts* (PCTs). PCTs are sometimes called Primary Care Organisations (PCOs), reflecting the change in the name (Primary Care Groups (PCG) became PCTs but are still organisations that commission primary care).

SHAs provide a framework for developing health and social care services across the range of local NHS organisations. Each SHA has a role in 'whole system planning' and performance management across organisational boundaries from primary and secondary care, and across all healthcare providers and networks for a specified number of PCTs in the local area.

PCTs are the lead NHS organisation in assessing need, planning and securing all health services and improving health for the population they serve. They lie at the heart of the reform process with its stated aim of 'decentralising' decision-making and putting the patient, through local health agencies, at the heart of the health system. They therefore have a key role to play in engaging with the local community including a range of stakeholders such as voluntary groups, education and housing authorities.

### PCT functions

PCTs have both a provider and a commissioning function. When they 'provide' they are responsible for both primary and community services. As commissioners of health care they deal with a greater plurality of healthcare providers, encouraged by a central government agenda. In the longer term, PCTs will probably focus more and more on commissioning, and less on providing more direct services such as district and community nurses or PCT-funded dental access centres. PCTs are currently responsible for 85 per cent of the NHS budget.

PCTs can be said to have three main functions:

1 ▷ **improving** the health of the community – assessing its health needs and preparing plans, tackling health inequalities, leading partnership working with local authorities and others

2 ▷ **developing** primary and community health services – managing and integrating all medical, dental, pharmaceutical and optical primary and community services as well as ensuring quality

3 ▷ **commissioning** services, either by themselves or in partnership with a local authority or through devolving indicative budgets to practice-based commissioners (see Chapter 3).[1]

The number of PCTs in England has recently been significantly reduced from the original 300 plus to approximately 150. Most are much larger, in the hope of obtaining greater co-ordination of services (especially emergency services), and larger PCTs will be able to have a stronger commissioning function. There is, still, a great discrepancy in the size of populations serviced, with some PCTs serving over a million people and some with populations of only 100,000.

The performance of each PCT is monitored by the SHA, and, in theory if not in practice, the PCTs are responsible for the performance of all its providers including general practices. This monitoring will be through clinical governance (see Chapter 4) and the monitoring laid down by the GMS2 contract and the payments for the Quality and Outcomes Framework. Increasingly PCTs are also responsible for managing the transition of general practice budgets to Practice-Based Commissioning (see Chapter 3).

The challenge for PCTs is to reconcile encouraging local decisions around commissioning whilst overseeing a consistency and equity of provision for its entire population. Inevitably the increased size of some PCTs has made it difficult for individual practices and individual GPs to feel they have a direct influence into commissioning decisions.

### *Primary care in the remaining home countries*

#### SCOTLAND

The population of Scotland is relatively well served in terms of general practice, with, in 2005, 77 whole-time equivalent GPs per 100,000 population as against 61 in England.

However, the managerial framework for the provision of primary care services is rather different. An increasingly devolved system overseen by the Scottish Parliament since 1999 has seen Scotland distance itself from any form of internal market. The underpinning philosophy is much more one of integration and collaboration.



In 2004 the separate provider trusts were abolished in favour of 14 *NHS boards* with the explicit aim of breaking down traditional barriers between primary and acute care. In the following year *Community Health Partnerships* (CHPs) were created to manage primary and community health services. In the larger boards several CHPs might exist around geographical areas and they serve as the focus for integrating primary and specialist services as well as linking with local authorities and the voluntary sector. There is a strong emphasis on preventive care and tackling health inequalities. The co-operative nature of the Scottish system offers great potential for closer working between the sectors and different parts of the system. Whilst this system appears to offer advantages in offering 'joined-up thinking' in providing care to the patient across his or her health service, some commentators have felt that the relative stability and lack of market pressures might cause a lack of challenge and contestability to the system, and so produce a less dynamic and change-oriented service.

#### WALES

Although the National Assembly of Wales has somewhat fewer devolved powers than Scotland there has been a distinct divergence of health policy in recent years with a search for more distinctly Welsh solutions to meet specific concerns in Wales, which has the UK's highest rates of cancer, heart disease and deprivation.

An overarching *Health and Social Care Department* with Regional Offices provides the central framework with service provision then being initiated through *Local Health Boards* (LHBs) and *NHS Trusts*. The latter represents the secondary care provision base with most of their income being derived from the LHBs. It is the LHBs that are perhaps the most directly comparable with PCTs in England. The LHBs are coterminous with local authorities and receive 75 per cent of the NHS Wales budget. The LHBs have strategic goals of building partnerships with other agencies and promoting improved health and public engagement. More specifically the LHBs are responsible for:

- commissioning and providing primary and community care health services
- commissioning secondary care services.

Wales has therefore retained elements of separation between commissioner and provider, and incorporated some central targets along with this. However, the rural nature of Wales and population distribution makes it difficult to foster a competitive culture other than in the larger urban centres.



### NORTHERN IRELAND

Since 1972 the NHS in Northern Ireland has been integrated with social services and thereby designated Health and Personal Social Services. More recently public safety has been incorporated resulting in the Department of Health, Social Services and Public Safety (DHSSPS). Difficulty in establishing the Northern Ireland Assembly has seen quite extended periods of direct rule from Westminster. Recently the creation of the Assembly and a wide-ranging Public Services Review has seen a transformation in the shape of services in Northern Ireland.

A small DHSSPS exists to set strategic policy. The Department will also contain a commissioning authority acting across the province as well as providing a performance management function. Local Commissioning Groups (LCGs) with a mix of GPs, healthcare professionals and lay representatives will provide local input.

The purchaser–provider separation therefore exists structurally. However, the number of provider trusts has been reduced from 18 to 5 so it is likely the focus of commissioning will be on contestability and establishing best value rather than a literal market system. Alongside the structural charges a greater use of targets is in evidence. Finally it is hoped that the LCGs will bring greater involvement of GPs, who have previously lacked a degree of integration with secondary care providers.

### *Implications for GPs within the health systems*

It might seem difficult for a patient who cannot understand why his or her GP cannot 'write' a prescription for a particular drug and why the 'NHS' has a right to stop the GP providing what the patient sees as a lifesaving drug. General practitioners do exist within the wider framework of primary care and this exists irrespective of the differences between systems. Inevitably policies, procedures and perhaps most explicitly targets will flow through bodies such as PCTs to hand onto the GP and primary care team. There is then for the individual GP a general challenge to participate effectively to both shape and deliver appropriate services, and to try and guide his or her patients through each system.

GPs will now find more specific roles within their particular health community such as leading the commissioning for a particular service, acting as a lead practice within a grouping of practices, or participating in care networks so that the primary care and GP perspective is properly valued. GPs will continue to serve at the interface between their colleagues (GPs and other members of the primary care team) as well as their patients and the system (PCTs, health board, etc.).

It is clear though that each of the systems described places more or less emphasis upon separation of the provider arm from the commissioning function. In England in particular the desire for integrated care might be difficult to achieve against the backdrop of an increasing variety of providers, as well as trying to commission meaningful services while secondary care is engaged in reconfiguration of services as part of its own survival plan.



### Questions

**1** ▷ What proportion of NHS funds are English PCTs responsible for?

**2** ▷ What role do SHAs play in the delivery of primary care?

**3** ▷ What role do PCTs have in the delivery of Practice-Based Commissioning?

**4** ▷ How does healthcare organisation in Scotland differ?

**5** ▷ How is health care organised in Wales?

**6** ▷ How is health care delivered in Northern Ireland?

**7** ▷ Which country's system is thought to have the most integrated approach?

**8** ▷ Which country's system is closest to a market-based approach?

#### Reference

1 • NHS Confederation. *The NHS in the UK 2006/07: a pocket guide* London: The NHS Confederation, 2006.

#### Further reading

Department of Health. *Shifting the Balance of Power with the NHS: securing delivery* London: DoH, 2001.

Department of Health. *Health and Personal Services Statistics 2002–3* London: DoH, 2003.

Offredy M. An exploratory study of the role and training needs of one Primary Care Trust's professional executive committee members *Primary Health Care Research and Development* 2005; **6**: 149–61.

# Commissioning and contracting

# 3

*Juliet Woodin and Elizabeth Wade*

### *Scenario*

*You have recently joined a practice that is part of an active Practice-Based Commissioning (PBC) cluster. You have been asked to take a lead for commissioning. The PBC cluster has identified a significant number of hospital admissions and outpatient attendances that it believes could be avoided, and more convenient services provided, if it could develop a wider range of services in primary care. There is a considerable amount of enthusiasm for this in some of the cluster practices, but others are concerned about the increased workload. The hospital is concerned that it will lose income as a result, and the PCT has been asking whether the clinical quality of the new services will be equivalent to those provided in hospital.*



## Introduction

Commissioning and contracting are significant features of the National Health Service (NHS) today, particularly in England. These activities impact on general practice in significant ways. This chapter will briefly introduce the concept of health service commissioning and its place in the NHS, describe the main components of commissioning and contracting, and discuss their relevance to general practice.

## Policy context

Commissioning and contracting became central to the organisation of the NHS following policy changes announced in the late 1980s.[1] Prior to this, the vast majority of hospital and community health services (HCHS) were delivered through a hierarchical, managerially integrated healthcare system. The creation of the internal market changed this into a system in which the function of planning and allocating healthcare funding was separated from that of providing health services. The role of deciding what hospital and community health services to fund, and allocating resources to providers accordingly, was given first to Health Authorities and General Practice Fundholders (GPFHs), then later transferred to Primary Care Groups (PCGs), Primary Care Trusts (PCTs) and, most recently, to Practice-Based Commissioners (PBCs).* Initially this task was referred to as 'purchasing' (reflecting the idea of the healthcare system as a market) but the term 'commissioning' (which, as described below, has broader connotations) gradually gained currency.

Although commissioning and provision were conceptually and organisationally split under this system, as the term 'internal market' suggests, both functions initially remained within the NHS. Recent policy has encouraged the development of more open, external markets, and the commissioning of secondary care and community services from a wider range of providers, including those from the commercial and voluntary sector.

The history of commissioning primary care services themselves is slightly different, because here responsibilities for funding and provision have always been organisationally separate, with practitioners providing services as contractors rather than as employees. However, the nature of this purchaser–provider relationship has also changed in recent years. In particular, since the introduction of the new (2004) GMS contract, the role of PCOs as commissioners (and not simply as passive funders) of general practice has been made much more explicit.



---

**What do we mean by 'commissioning' and 'contracting'?**

The terms 'commissioning' and 'contracting' and related terms such as 'purchasing' and 'procurement' are much used in the NHS but their meaning is contested and there is no single universally agreed definition. In this chapter, for the sake of clarity and consistency, we will use the terms commissioning and contracting as those most central to contemporary healthcare policy and management. However, it should be kept in mind that in some policy and management documentation and dialogue other terms might be used to describe the same activities.

Commissioning is defined here as 'the set of linked activities required to assess the healthcare needs of a population, specify the services required to meet those needs within a strategic framework, secure those services, monitor and evaluate the outcomes'.[2] It is important to note that the commissioning role is, therefore, a *proactive, strategic* one, in which the commissioner

*Following devolution in 1999 the health systems of England, Scotland, Wales and Northern Ireland diverged. Commissioning in general, and Practice-Based Commissioning in particular, are much more features of the English system than the other countries. Inevitably therefore the discussion of commissioning in this chapter will refer most directly to England.

intervenes and engages with suppliers to shape and design services, informed by his or her understanding of local health needs. As such it is distinguished from the more reactive process of purchasing whatever 'off the shelf' services providers have decided to offer.

As well as being strategic and proactive, commissioning is an ongoing and iterative process. Consequently, many writers have referred to the idea of the commissioning 'cycle', a concept reflected in several recent policy documents.[3] A simplified commissioning cycle is illustrated in Figure 3.1.

Figure 3.1 ○ ***The commissioning cycle***

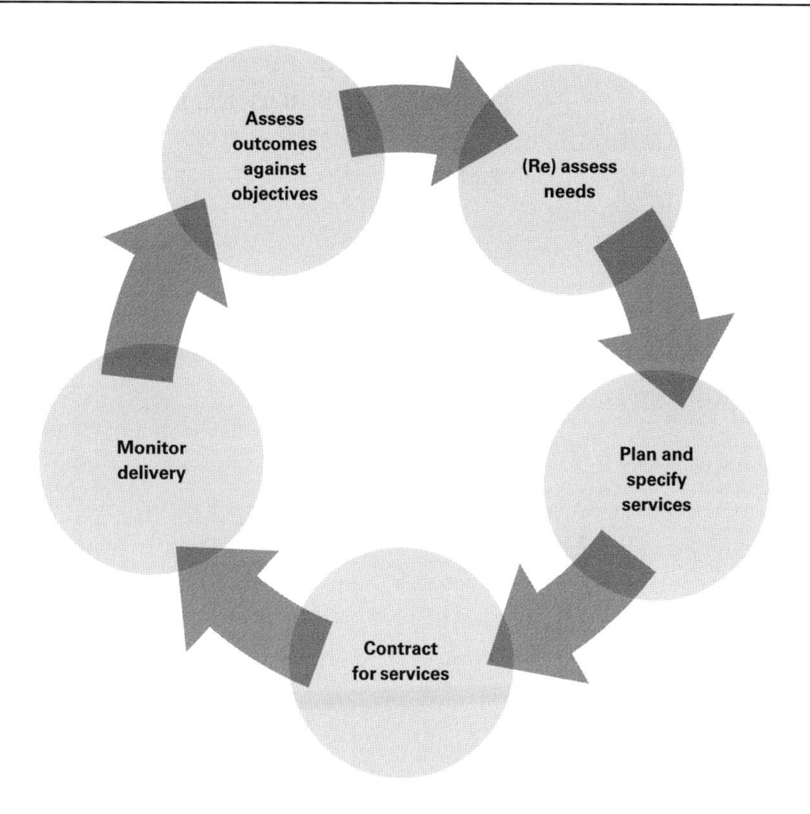


In the real world it is seldom possible to follow this cycle consistently and neatly in the order suggested. However, these basic principles summarise the commissioning task: planning services and interventions on the basis of an understanding of needs; clearly specifying requirements and agreeing the terms under which they will be delivered with service providers; and monitoring and evaluating outcomes to inform future decision-making and practice.

Under this description, contracting is just one part of the commissioning cycle. It is used here to mean 'the technical process of selecting a provider, negotiating and agreeing the terms of a contract for services, and ongoing management of the contract including payment, monitoring, and variations'.[2] Contracting is subject to various legal and/or regulatory requirements, and, as such, is generally seen as a more clearly defined activity than commissioning as a whole, and some of its other elements. It is becoming more critical for NHS commissioners to understand the legal and procedural aspects of contracting as they commission more services from the non-statutory sector.

## Commissioning, contracting and general practice

The position of general practice in relation to commissioning and contracting is complex. On the one hand, the practice is a *provider* of primary healthcare services, commissioned by a PCO through one of the types of contract described in Chapter 1. On the other hand, the practice is a *commissioner* of hospital and community health services through PBC. This dual role as both provider and commissioner creates both opportunities and challenges.

The remainder of this chapter will consider these roles and challenges in more detail, highlighting the importance of the PCO in creating the overall framework within which they operate.



## The practice as provider

PCOs are responsible for ensuring that everyone living in their area has access to primary medical services that meet required standards. Although PCOs directly provide primary medical care in some circumstances, they usually meet this requirement by agreeing contracts with a number of independent GP practices, who then deliver services on their behalf.

Until relatively recently, these contracts were nationally negotiated and funded. All practices across the country therefore had the same terms and conditions, and the role of the PCO (or previously the Health Authority) was a relatively passive one, with responsibility for paying and auditing practices, and resolving local operational issues, but not for the strategic planning and specification of primary care provision.

This situation began to change with the introduction of PMS contracts in the late 1990s. As described in Chapter 1, PMS contracts are locally negotiated and funded. They were designed to enable PCOs to more directly influence the type, location and standard of primary care services in situations where the national contract was not sufficiently flexible to meet specific local needs. When the new GMS contracts were introduced in 2004, PCOs were also handed responsibility for funding and managing these at a local level, so that all independent practices are now directly accountable to a PCO through their contract. At the same time, PCOs were given new powers to commission primary care from Alternative Provider Medical Services under APMS contracts. As a result, PCOs now have a much more proactive role as strategic commissioners of primary care: shaping the local market of primary care provision; holding independent practices to account for the quality of services they provide; and encouraging the entrance of new providers to the market where necessary.

There are three levels of services that PCOs might commission from general practices:



### *Essential services*

These are the 'core' services that all practices must provide to any patient that is registered with them (and to non-registered patients if their need is 'immediate and necessary'), including health assessment and screening, medical treatment, advice, or referral on to more specialist health services.

### *Additional services*

These are also core primary care services to which all patients are entitled, and PCTs must therefore commission them from some source. However, individual practices can opt out of providing these if, for example, they do not have the relevant skills or training. Additional services include contraceptive services, cervical screening, maternity services and minor surgery.

### *Enhanced services*

These are services that, although suitable to be provided in a primary care setting, go beyond the definition of core or essential primary care. They may be nationally or locally specified, and will be commissioned by PCOs according to local need and demand for such services. Examples might include more advanced or complex minor surgery, and services provided with GPs with a Special Interest (GPwSIs).

The type of primary medical services contract that is agreed between a practice and the PCO depends on a number of factors including the status of the provider (i.e. whether they are part of the 'NHS family' or not), and determines which of these services they must or can provide. For example, PCOs can not force existing General Medical Services (GMS) practices to provide services beyond those specified as essential (although the practice might well choose to do so), while they could make the provision of additional and enhanced services a particular requirement of a PMS or APMS contract (this is what makes a PMS or APMS contract a more flexible option for a PCO).

This section has briefly outlined the relationship between a PCO as commissioner of primary care services and the practice as provider. The next goes on to explore the commissioning role of practices themselves, then considers how these two roles increasingly interact.

---

## The practice as commissioner



The provision of primary medical services might be seen as the first and foremost function of general practices. However, as described above, practices have also been commissioners in various forms since the 1990s, first through GPFH, where practices were allowed, and indeed encouraged, to hold and manage a budget to purchase health care for their patients. Initially this was restricted to the budget for elective surgery, but subsequently additional services were added and some practices, known as the Total Purchasing Pilots,[4] took on virtually the whole budget for their patients' care. Other practices preferred to work on a collective basis to influence secondary care, a model known as locality commissioning,[5] which gained official government support with the election of the Labour government in 1997, and later became the basis for PCGs and their successors, PCTs. The Labour government withdrew the GPFH option in 1997, but signalled, in several policy statements, an intention that individual practices should again be able to hold their own budgets, before making a firm announcement in *The NHS Improvement Plan* in June 2004[6] followed by the first formal guidance on PBC later that year.[7]

The Department of Health has described PBC as shown in Box 3.1.

PBC is stated by the Department of Health to be voluntary for practices, but they are actively encouraged to take part. The primary incentive for practices to take part in PBC is the potential to save and reinvest resources to improve care for their patients. However, in the early stages of PBC a national incentive scheme was made available to encourage participation by providing some payment for the time and resources that would need to be expended by practices to develop their plans. This national scheme has been replaced by local incentive schemes agreed between PCTs and their practices from 2007 onwards.

Box 3.1 ○ ***Practice-Based Commissioning definitions***

- First, commissioning is the process by which the health needs of a population are assessed, responsibility is taken for ensuring that appropriate services are available which meet these needs (including delivery of national local NHS planning framework targets), and accountability for the associated health outcomes is established. PBC transfers these responsibilities, along with the associated budget, from the PCT to primary care clinicians, including nurses. They will determine the range of services to be provided for their population with the PCT acting as their agent to undertake any required procurements and to carry out the administrative tasks to underpin these processes.[8]
- Second, PBC is about engaging practices and other primary care professionals in the commissioning of services. Through PBC, frontline clinicians are being provided with the resources and support to become more involved in commissioning decisions. Under PBC, practices receive information on how their patients use health services. This information can be used for the redesign of services by frontline clinicians for the benefit of patients. See www.dh.gov.uk/en/Policyandguidance/Organisationpolicy/Commissioning/Practice-basedcommissioning/DH_4138698.



Practices can engage in PBC individually, but in most parts of the country they have clustered together into groups, consortia, or in some cases legal entities such as companies or social enterprises, for the purposes of commissioning. This grouping of practices helps to share the workload, the financial risk, and the available expertise.

## ***Practice-Based Commissioning: aims***

PBC is founded in the recognition that primary care clinicians are responsible, through their referral decisions and other activities, for committing the majority of NHS resources. The aim of PBC is to make primary care clinicians more aware of the financial consequences of their clinical decisions and to give them the information and incentives to use resources differently. This is often referred to as 'clinical engagement'. In doing this, it is anticipated that a number of benefits will be achieved, including tailoring services more to the needs of the local community, improving the quality and choice of services, providing more convenient and individualised services for patients, especially those with long-term conditions, and ensuring the best use of public money.

### *Practice-Based Commissioning: budgets*

Practice-Based Commissioners are given a budget by the PCT that should be the practice's share of the total PCT budget. Certain elements, such as for the overhead costs of the PCT, are then blocked back to the PCT. This transferred budget is an *indicative* budget (as was the case with GPFH and locality commissioning). This means that the practice sees the total resources available, receives information about the expenditure against them, and takes decisions about the future use of the budget, but the legal accountability for the budget remains with the PCT.

### *Practice-Based Commissioning: service redesign*

The major incentive to take part in PBC is the potential to improve services for patients, particularly by redesigning the 'patient pathway' so that their patients receive the package of care that will best deliver outcomes and quality of care while representing value for money.



A compendium of 'good practice' published just prior to the first tranche of PBC guidance contained numerous examples of service improvements that contributors felt had resulted from clinical engagement in commissioning and service redesign processes.[9]

More recently, a number of tools and techniques have been developed to assist practices in reviewing their referrals to elective services, and reducing unnecessary demand on non-elective secondary care services,[3] some drawing on practice in other countries.

### *Practice-Based Commissioning: responsibilities and requirements*

Once participating in PBC there are certain procedures and guidelines that practices and clusters are expected to follow as they begin to manage their budgets and plan changes in services. These include the following:

- ▷ agreeing an annual commissioning plan with their PCT, setting out their commissioning objectives
- ▷ submitting individual business cases for approval by the PCT for any new services they wish to develop and provide through PBC
- ▷ agreeing the use of any freed-up resources with the PCT
- ▷ playing their full part in meeting national and local priorities as well as responding to their own patients' needs
- ▷ involving patients in developing their plans, and making their plans available for public scrutiny
- ▷ working in partnership with their PCT, local authority, other health

professionals, and other organisations within the local health community
- having agreed their indicative budgets, manage within them, and to contribute to financial risk-sharing pools where appropriate.

Practice-Based Commissioners can expect their PCTs to support them in a variety of ways. These include:

- provision of a local incentive scheme
- a fair budget
- facilitating retention by the practice of 70 per cent of any savings, to be invested in patient services
- provision to practices of timely and accurate activity, and financial information relating to the practice
- supporting their commissioning activities through the provision of appropriate skills and services.



There are a number of areas of commissioning that practices are not expected to undertake. Analysis suggests that some services require a larger population base for commissioning than a practice or even PBC cluster.[10] Specialised services, for conditions that have relatively low prevalence, often require costly treatments, and are provided by specialist tertiary centres. These are therefore commissioned by consortia of PCTs that enable the necessary commissioning expertise to be developed and financial risk to be managed across a large population base.[3]

The PCT carries the legal responsibility for the commissioning budgets devolved to practices, and will be the legal party to any contracts and agreements made. The contracting elements of commissioning, such as the formal negotiation, agreement, and signing of contracts and agreements with providers, and their subsequent monitoring and variation, are carried out by PCTs on behalf of PBC. These agreements should reflect the wishes of Practice-Based Commissioners in terms of the package of services to be provided, but the PCT-level arrangements ensure that these requirements are incorporated in single contracts with each provider, thus limiting transaction costs, and making best use of legal, financial and managerial expertise.

Neither Practice-Based Commissioners nor PCTs negotiate prices with providers. These are set nationally in the form of a national tariff for procedures, based on related diagnostic groups, which is updated annually.

In summary, PBC offers practices an opportunity to reshape the services their patients receive. In some cases, practices can achieve this by influencing existing providers to work in different ways, or by commissioning services from new or alternative providers who they believe will better meet their patients' needs. In many cases, however, a practice (or cluster of practices) will decide to reshape pathways by taking on additional work themselves in primary care. This could take various forms. At the simplest level individual practices might each agree to provide a more intensive level of care for patients with certain conditions to reduce the need for onward referral, thus reducing their expenditure in secondary care. For example, practices might start to initiate insulin therapy for patients with diabetes, when they would previously have referred such cases to a hospital clinic. At the other end of the spectrum, a group of practices could formally establish a limited company to provide a range of primary care-based resources (such as GPwSIs), as an alternative to hospital provision. Whatever the model for doing so, it is clear that this is the point at which the relationship between the provider and commissioner role of a practice potentially becomes complex. As a result of the commissioning decisions they make, practices might want or need to change the boundaries of their own roles as service providers.



## Bringing it all together

As will be evident from the accounts above, being both a commissioner and a provider of services puts practices in a strong position to take and implement wise and informed decisions about the pattern of care their patients receive. Daily contact with patients, and the information about patients' health held by the practice, give great insight into both health needs and the quality of current services. Through the services the practice provides directly, and the referral decisions of the doctors, the practice can influence the use of secondary care services by patients and thus affect the expenditure of the commissioning budget. However, being both commissioner and provider also creates some tensions that need to be managed.

## Managing conflicts of interest

In the first place, there might be a conflict of interest if a practice wishes to redirect the commissioning budget to services provided by the practice. If such a change in service has a beneficial effect (even indirectly) on the financial health of the practice, practices will need to ensure that the change is being made in the interests of patients and not solely for the benefit of the practice.

Second, when patient flows are redirected, the income of hospital and other providers might be affected by decisions made by Practice-Based Commissioners. While this is not a problem in principle (indeed the NHS reforms as a whole seek to incentivise providers to improve by encouraging patients and GPs to vote with their feet and enabling the money to follow the patient) if the practice itself benefits from the move, it will be essential to show that the move offers clear benefits to patients. Furthermore, practices will wish to be aware of any impact of changes on the financial viability of hospital providers as a whole, since their patients are likely to rely on these hospitals for a wide range of other services.

---

## The role of the PCT

The PCT, as the statutory body responsible for health care in its area, will be held ultimately accountable for the decisions taken by Practice-Based Commissioners. It thus needs to combine its support to PBC with an important role in ensuring that these real or perceived conflicts are managed well, and providing challenge to PBC where necessary. It does this in a number of ways, including by:

- requiring business cases to be submitted for the provision of new services, for PCT approval. It is likely that the Professional Executive Committee of the PCT will play a key role in the approval process, and will itself need to have clear procedural rules and ensure that practitioners with an interest in any proposal exclude themselves from decisions[3]
- ensuring that patients are able to exercise choice of provider when needing elective care, through encouraging new providers and publishing details of choices for patients and practitioners
- using competitive tendering processes for new services where appropriate. There is detailed guidance about the circumstances where tendering is required[11] but in essence this will usually only be in the case of services being moved out of hospital wholesale where new monopoly provision is created within the PCT area. The Department of Health expects such occasions to be infrequent
- benchmarking costs and prices for services that are not subject to the national tariff to ensure value for money, and by publication of prices
- engaging Practice-Based Commissioners in the creation of an overall strategy for the development of services and providers within the area, which practices can then use as a framework for their own commissioning plans
- collating PBC plans and making them available to the Local Authority Overview and Scrutiny Committee.

Practice-Based Commissioners can develop their own arrangements to help avoid and manage any real or perceived conflicts of interest, for instance by ensuring that patients and the local community are involved in their commissioning plans and are fully informed about any changes, and by managing their relationships with other providers in a mature way. By auditing and evaluating the results of changes driven through PBC, and by seeking out and sharing learning from these changes, practices will be seen as responsible and accountable commissioners. Relationships between Practice-Based Commissioners and their PCT are key to the successful implementation of PBC, and a mutual understanding and respect for their roles and contributions will help to achieve this.

---

## The evidence



From their attempts to encourage and incentivise participation in PBC, it is clear that policy-makers see the involvement of primary care as critical to commissioning and to the achievement of health system reform.

However, the question of whether commissioning and contracting are effective processes for improving the performance of health systems at all, and exactly what the role of primary care might be within this, is actually very difficult to answer. A review of evidence from Europe, the USA and New Zealand found that commissioning is not done consistently well in any of these systems.[12] This may in part be because none of these countries take a systematic approach to commissioning, as is being attempted in England. The development of commissioning in the UK has been subject to evaluation.[10,13] From their review of the evidence, Smith and colleagues concluded:

- ▷ there is little substantive research evidence to demonstrate that any commissioning approach has made a significant or strategic impact on secondary care services
- ▷ primary care-led commissioning (where clinicians have clear influence over budgets) can however secure improved responsiveness such as shorter waiting times, as was seen with GP fundholding
- ▷ primary care-led commissioning made its biggest impact in primary and intermediate care, for example in developing a wide range of practice-based services
- ▷ highly determined managers and clinicians are able to use commissioning to change longstanding working practices in the local health system, as demonstrated in the total purchasing projects

- ▷ primary care commissioners can effect change in prescribing practice as demonstrated through GP commissioning and GP fundholding
- ▷ primary care-led commissioning increases transaction costs within commissioning.

While these conclusions are somewhat mixed in their assessment of the impact of commissioning, they do provide evidence to support a key role for primary care in commissioning.

## The future

In the light of the mixed evidence regarding the effectiveness of commissioning, there is considerable debate amongst academics and professionals about whether this is a good way of organising health care, and what the best way of managing the commissioning process itself might be. At the time of writing, government policy (in health care and other sectors) appears strongly committed to the notion that effective commissioning is key to public service reform and modernisation. The recent policy initiative to develop world-class commissioning in health confirms this, and reinforces the role of PBC.[14] However, the detail of policy and practice in these areas is constantly evolving, and keeping up to date with development through the websites below is recommended.

## Useful websites

**NHS Alliance** • www.nhsalliance.org.

**National Association of Primary Care** • www.napc.co.uk.

**NHS Primary Care Contracting site** • www.primarycarecontracting.nhs.uk.

**The Improvement Foundation** • www.improvementfoundation.org.

**Department of Health commissioning pages** • www.dh.gov.uk/en/Policyandguidance/Organisationpolicy/Commissioning.

**Care Services Improvement Partnership Better Commissioning Network** • www.cat.csip.org.uk.

## Questions

1 ▷ What are the objectives of PBC?

2 ▷ What is the difference between commissioning and contracting?

3 ▷ What is meant by the commissioning cycle and what are the processes within it?

4 ▷ What are the roles of the PCT in relation to PBC?

5 ▷ What benefits and challenges are associated with working together with other practices for the purposes of PBC?

6 ▷ What organisational arrangements are available for a PBC cluster?

7 ▷ What responsibilities does holding a PBC budget entail?



8 ▷ What information does the practice require in order to commission effectively?

9 ▷ What mechanisms could be used to involve patients in commissioning?

10 ▷ What are the differences between nGMS, PMS and APMS contracts?

11 ▷ Under what circumstances is the PCT required to put out to tender additional services proposed in primary care?

12 ▷ What is the purpose of the PBC business plan?

13 ▷ Why should a practice evaluate its redesigned services?

### References

1 • Department of health. *Working for Patients* London: HMSO, 1989 (Cm 555).

2 • Woodin J. Healthcare commissioning and contracting. In: K Walshe, J Smith (eds). *Healthcare Management* Maidenhead: Open University Press, 2006, pp. 201–23.

3 • Department of Health. *Health Reform in England: update and commissioning framework* London: DoH, 2006.

4 • Mays N. *The Purchasing of Health Care by Primary Health Care Organizations: an evaluation and guide to future policy* Buckingham: Open University Press, 2001.

5 • Black D G, Birchall A D, Trimble IMG. Non-fundholding in Nottingham: a vision of the future *British Medical Journal* 1994; **309(6959)**: 930–2.

6 • Department of Health. *The NHS Improvement Plan: putting people at the heart of public services* London: DoH, 2004 (Cm 6268).

7 • Department of Health. *Practice Based Commissioning: promoting clinical engagement* London: DoH, 2004.

8 • Department of Health. *Making Practice Based Commissioning a Reality: technical guidance* London: DoH, 2005.

9 • NHS Alliance. *Can Do!* Retford: NHS Alliance, 2004.

10 • Smith J, Mays N, Dixon J, *et al. A Review of the Effectiveness of Primary Care-Led Commissioning and Its Place in the NHS* London: The Health Foundation, 2004.

11 • Department of Health. *Practice Based Commissioning: practical implementation* London: DoH, 2006.

12 • Ham C. *Health Care Commissioning in the International Context: lessons from experience and evidence* Birmingham: Health Services Management Centre, University of Birmingham, 2008.

13 • Le Grand J, Mays N, Mulligan J-A. *Learning from the NHS Internal Market: a review of the evidence* London: King's Fund Publishing, 1998.

14 • Department of Health/Commissioning. *World Class Commissioning: vision* London: DoH, 2007.

# Managing performance in general practice

# 4

## The role of clinical governance, the National Patient Safety Authority, National Clinical Assessment Service and revalidation

*Veronica Wilkie*



### Scenario

*You are discussing with your trainer what you are going to do. You have seen that there is a 'long-term' locum in a nearby practice. The trainer says that one of the doctors had had some difficulties and is off work whilst things are being looked into. This starts a discussion on how GPs who find themselves in difficulty are identified and helped.*

### Introduction

> *In the great majority of cases, the causes of serious failures stretch far beyond the actions of the individuals immediately involved. Safety is a dynamic, not a static situation. In a socially and technically complex field such as healthcare, a huge number of factors are at work at any one time which influence the likelihood of failure.*
>
> (*An Organisation with a Memory*)[1]

Doctors are as human as the rest of the population, and will suffer from ill health as much as any other human being. Doctors are also at risk of becoming out of date, or working in chaotic systems that make it difficult for safe practice. This chapter looks at some of the safeguards that are put in place by the NHS to reduce this and what an individual doctor can do to protect the safety of his or her health and that of the patients being treated.

### Clinical governance

Clinical governance was introduced at the end of the 1990s in response to concerns following some high-profile cases. Although doctors had long been accountable to their professional regulatory bodies, doctors are now accountable to their colleagues and the Primary Care Organisation (PCO) for whom they work, the PCO also having a responsibility to the patients.[2] Although individuals in health care will continue to be accountable for individual patients, dealt with by the Laws of Negligence, clinical governance exists to hold groups of professionals to account for each other's performance, and recognises the role a 'system' of health care has in an individual healthcare worker's performance. When he wrote about clinical governance in 1998, Liam Donaldson, then Regional Director for the NHS Executive (Northern and Yorkshire), described clinical governance as having echoes of corporate governance,[3] an initiative aimed at redressing failed standards in industry through the Cadbury report.[4]

Clinical governance was described as having the following summary points:[3]

- clinical governance is to be the main vehicle for continuously improving the quality of patient care and developing the capacity of the NHS in England to maintain high standards (including dealing with poor professional performance)
- it requires organisation-wide transformation. Clinical leadership and positive organisational cultures are particularly important
- local professional self-regulation will be the key to dealing with the complex problems of poor performance among clinicians
- new approaches are needed to enable the recognition and replication of good clinical practice to ensure that lessons are reliably learnt from failures in standards of care.

Donaldson[3] went on to say that clinical governance should be:

- rigorous in its application
- organisation-wide in its emphasis
- accountable in its delivery
- developmental in its thrust
- positive in its connotations.

At the time it was hailed as being the most important quality initiative that had come out of the NHS. Doctors who have worked in the system only in the last 10 years might find it hard to envisage working in a healthcare system without many checks and balances to its practitioners.

Figure 4.1 ○ ***Variation in the quality of health organisations***

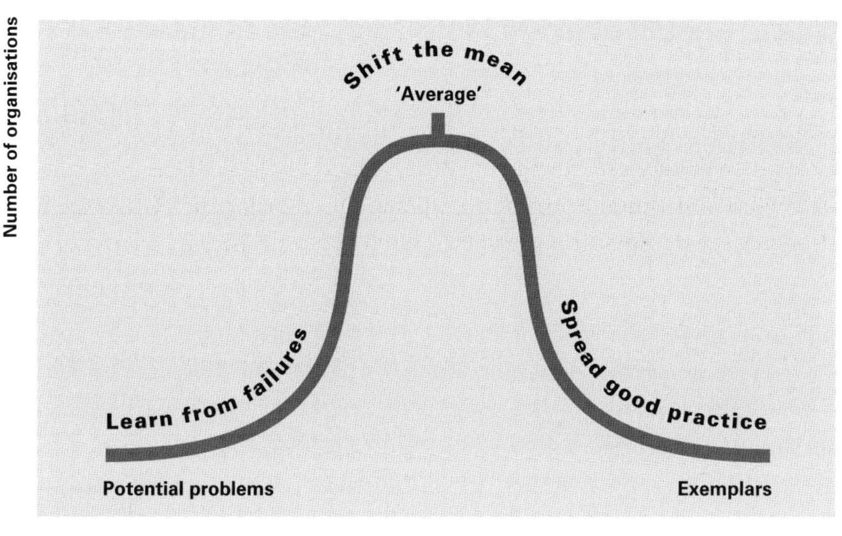


*Source*: Scally G, Donaldson L. Looking forward: clinical governance and the drive for quality improvement in the new NHS in England *British Medical Journal* 1998; **317**: 61–5.[3] Reproduced with permission from the BMJ Publishing Group.



Figure 4.1 illustrates how organisations can differ in how health care is practised, but through an integrated system can learn from other organisations, ideally before patients are put at risk.

At its best clinical governance will identify best practice and spread the word so that poor practice is halted. It should be inclusive and should involve everyone in health care. It has been described as 'doing anything and everything required to maximise quality'.[5]

The knowledge required for GPs is further expanded in the RCGP's curriculum statement 3.1 – *Clinical Governance*.[6] In essence clinical governance has seven 'pillars':

▷ clinical effectiveness
▷ risk management effectiveness
▷ patient experience
▷ communication effectiveness
▷ resource effectiveness
▷ strategic effectiveness
▷ leadership effectiveness.

These seven pillars are embedded in:

- ▷ system awareness
- ▷ teamwork
- ▷ communication
- ▷ ownership
- ▷ leadership.

---

## The role of audit

The implementation of clinical audit in the NHS had been patchy but was increasing steadily by the year 2000. There had been some examples of how audit was transforming chronic disease care, with UK GPs and their increasingly sophisticated use of computers leading the way. However, concerns had been raised about how audit processes across the NHS had failed to detect and moderate significant clinical failures.[7] Audit is still central to clinical governance but should be integrated and used as a developmental tool, with multiprofessional learning, problem-based learning and through discussion of significant events.

Audit can be used as a tool for instituting change. Using the simplest audit cycle (see Figure 4.2), various initiatives can be instigated and then evaluated using the Plan–Do–Study–Act model. Individual clinicians can also audit their consultation times and prescribing habits, and use this to develop a Personal Development Plan (PDP).



---

## Clinical governance in the practice

There are many ways in which a practice can look to clinical governance. The NHS website www.cgsupport.nhs.uk/Resources/default.asp is a useful site for resources, and the practice clinical governance lead can access the Primary Care Clinical Governance Team for advice and examples of good practice. The Clinical Governance Support Team was set up at the end of 1999 to support the implementation of clinical governance within the NHS. The team's aims are to:

- ▷ work with partner organisations to build on the development of appraisal, and to strengthen revalidation
- ▷ support frontline primary care to embed clinical governance and improve the patient experience
- ▷ provide an online education and training package.[8]

Figure 4.2 ○ ***The PDSA audit cycle, showing an example of how patient access can be reviewed***

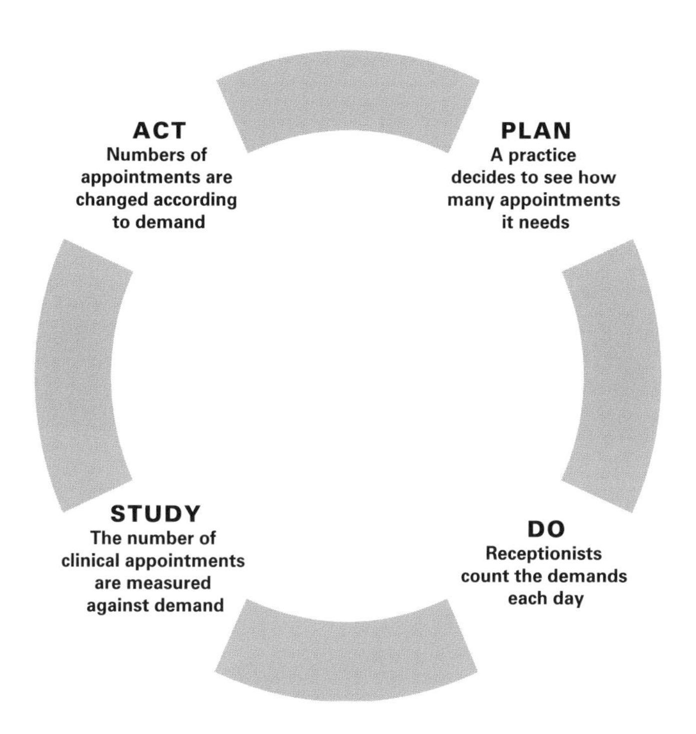




All practices should have a 'lead' for clinical governance, which is usually one of the partners with the practice manager. These individuals will be responsible for setting the agenda within the practice. Ways in which this can be achieved are:

### *Culture*

The culture is vital to good governance. A good culture is necessary for effective teamworking, facilitating successful meetings and enabling a practice to embrace change. All healthcare professionals should feel supported if they encounter a problem and patients have the right to expect problems are dealt with fairly and professionally. Clinical governance is not only about looking at problems but also about reflecting on services offered and clinical practice, or practice systems and celebrating good practice. Clinical governance is also about providing a safe working environment and developing a *learning organisation*. Clinical governance leads should strive to provide a safe and supportive space for events to be discussed, with appropriate follow-up. There are two myths to dispel when creating a suitable culture: that if people try hard enough they will not make any errors and if you punish people they will make fewer mistakes.[9]

### Communication

Ensuring communication between patients and healthcare staff and between team members is vital. The clinical governance leads should ensure safe practice in notes recording and message handling, whilst ensuring confidentiality. Communication with the PCT Clinical Governance Team is also vital; most PCTs will run education and training events for practice staff and are on hand to give advice if needed. Does the practice share its learning? Is there space for clinicians to discuss their learning outcomes with their colleagues? Is there space and time for more informal communication between staff and other members of the healthcare team, allowing for the 'I saw your patient Mr X this morning and I was wondering if ...' discussions to be held.



### Evidence-Based Practice

Providing staff with enough time to keep up to date (clinically and managerially) whilst ensuring continuity of care is always a balancing act, but vital. Consider whether all staff have enough study leave. There is an overwhelming amount of evidence that learning can be enhanced through practice-based discussions, rather than individuals disappearing out of the practice all the time. Clinical guidelines have a tendency to multiply on a GP's desk so why not lighten this task by sharing the load?

### Patient involvement

Increasingly NHS organisations are using patients to guide services and learning. It is recognised that patient-based clinical events can aid further learning, but it might be worth thinking about asking patients to talk to the practice about their experiences. How does the practice appear from the outside? The NHS Clinical Governance Team has many examples to share.

### Personal and Practice Development Plans

One of the best ways to generate discussion is to discuss each clinician's personal learning plan and then look at developing a Practice Development Plan (PDP). Are all the practice-based learning needs met? Have sufficient outside inputs to this been covered, such as:

- ▷ local PCT priorities
- ▷ patient complaint reviews
- ▷ national priorities, NICE guidance and National Service Frameworks.

The team should discuss how their skills are represented in the practice team, e.g. is there the correct skill mix within the practice? If retirements are imminent is there any aspect that an existing team member can learn to do? Are there complementary skills across all the teams?

There is always a risk that clinicians will fill their PDPs with subjects they are interested in, and whilst it is important to keep up with developments in areas of interests it is also important to understand areas of need. There are many ways of identifying these. The annually held appraisal is one, while discussions with peers of cases and significant events is another. There is an increasing number of electronic tools, such as the RCGP PEP eKit, that can also act as an aid to identifying learning needs. Some GPs find keeping a log of questions they are unable to answer for patients useful (PUNs and DENs – Patient's Unmet Needs, Doctor's Educational Needs). In many PCTs individual appraisals are often with individuals across a whole year, so meeting once or twice a year to inform PDP development of individual plans as well as practice plans can be very helpful.



### Complaints

Meaningful reaction to complaints is vital. Whether the complaint is about a system or a clinical matter, every person will make mistakes, but repeated mistakes might be a sign of a poor system or problems with an individual. The practice should have a robust system not only for collecting complaints but also for dealing with them in a timely and appropriate manner. More serious complaints involving risk to patient safety should be dealt with as a priority involving the PCT or the General Medical Council (GMC) according to severity (see pp. 53–5).

### Good teamwork

Good teamwork and team dynamics are vital to communication and the dynamics of the practice and its culture. More has been discussed in Chapter 8 but can be summarised in this context as:

- ▷ a common and shared purpose
- ▷ clear goals for all contributors
- ▷ open communication
- ▷ opportunities for team members to develop their skills.[10]

### *Good record keeping*

Good record keeping is vital for patient safety and multiprofessional management of patient care. Made easier in today's use of IT systems, the information is only as good as the person entering it. Therefore clear guidance on how to enter data and which codes to use are vital, so that audit can aid improvement. How data from external sources (hospital letters, patient communication) are stored and made accessible is also important for safe practice. All NHS organisations should have a *'Caldicott Guardian'*. This is an individual who takes responsibility for the confidentiality of the record-keeping and the steps to doing this. Clear advice on this can be found at: www.connectingforhealth.nhs.uk/systemsandservices/infogov/caldicott/caldresources/guidance/caldicott_2006.pdf.

### *Significant Event Audit*



Significant Event Audits (sometimes called Critical Event Reviews or Analyses) are now embedded in clinical governance culture. The current GMS2 GP contract has a requirement for significant events to be discussed and to include deaths and suicides as part of the Quality and Outcomes Framework. Significant events might be large (a suicide) or small, a lost message, related to patients or to the smooth running of the practice (e.g. safe storage of personal items). Clear recording and clear follow-up with named 'champions' to take changes forward and report back are essential. Suitable questions to be asked at the review might be:

- ▷ what happened? Did something go wrong? What things went well?
- ▷ how did it affect the patient, you, and the practice?
- ▷ could it have been avoided?
- ▷ can it be stopped from happening again? What action needs to be taken by whom and when?
- ▷ what learning or development need has this highlighted for you (to put into your PDP)?
- ▷ what learning or personal development need has it highlighted for others?

Keeping a log of all critical incidents can help identify patterns. If you re-audit an event you can see whether you put into place the changes you agreed in the review.

### *Accountability*

With the introduction of clinical governance came a stronger accountability for patient safety, not only for the individual clinicians, but also for managers,

PCOs, hospital trusts and the wider NHS. Individuals or practices identifying problems to the PCO should in theory be able to receive some help and back-up to rectify them. Persistent poor performance in an individual also becomes the responsibility of the practice and the PCO, and latterly 'integrated governance' has been described as a way of trust boards ensuring safe practice within the multiplicity of healthcare providers that are now being commissioned.

Integrated governance is a process that spans the various functional governance processes that are often unlinked and result in the handling of issues in silos. It is clear that all healthcare organisations need to demonstrate that they have strengthened and streamlined their governance arrangements within their organisations and, over time, develop a further integration between health and social care organisations in their health community. Integrated governance offers boards the opportunity to rethink their governance arrangements to be fit for the future direction of the NHS.[11]

Corporate governance was identified early on and outlined in 1999, the principles being:

- **accountability** ○ everything done by those who work in the NHS must be able to stand the test of parliamentary scrutiny, public judgements on propriety and professional codes of conduct
- **probity** ○ there should be an absolute standard of honesty in dealing with the assets of the NHS; integrity should be the hallmark of all personal conduct in decisions affecting patients, staff and suppliers, and in the use of information acquired in the course of NHS duties
- **openness** ○ there should be sufficient transparency about NHS activities to promote confidence between the NHS authority or trust and its staff, patients and the public.[12]

As PBC gathers momentum, groups of practices with budgets that run into tens of millions of pounds will find themselves under the same scrutiny for financial, corporate as well as clinical governance, as PCOs and hospital trusts have done before them.

### *Leadership*

Good and clear leadership has been shown to provide the basis for a culture that is dynamic and supportive. Without leadership, individuals might continue to 'do their own thing', which will leave the practice as an organisation at risk of skill deficits, and of being unable to produce a meaningful practice development to back up future business planning. Leadership is best shared and disseminated, engaging all staff and giving ownership of projects and clinical areas across the team, each lead being encouraged to communicate to the rest.

In summary clinical governance can be described as the unification and integration of harmonisation of six key systems:

- risk management
- performance management
- quality improvement
- information
- accountability
- communication.[13]

---

## The National Patient Safety Authority



The National Patient Safety Authority (NPSA) was set up in 2002 as a Special Health Authority created to co-ordinate the efforts of all those involved in health care, and, more importantly, to learn from adverse incidents occurring in the NHS. As well as making sure that incidents are reported in the first place, the NPSA is aiming to promote an open and fair culture in hospitals and across the health service, encouraging doctors and other staff to report incidents and 'near misses', when things almost go wrong. A key aim is to encourage staff to report incidents without fear of personal reprimand and know that by sharing their experiences others will be able to learn lessons and improve patient safety. The change of emphasis is more about the 'how' than the 'who'. It was set up after a report in 2000, *An Organisation with a Memory* by Professor Sir Liam Donaldson,[1] and was a response to the observation that the NHS failed to systematically learn from adverse events. It is hoped that, by systematically collecting and analysing adverse events, risks are identified and work is undertaken on producing solutions to prevent harm. The RCGP curriculum statement 3.2 *Patient Safety* offers guidance, including identifying when a Patient Safety Incident (PSI) should be openly discussed, with the patient, family and wider healthcare organisation.[14,15]

The NPSA produced *Seven Steps To Patient Safety* as a best practice guide, and has further refined it for primary care.[16] They cite these steps as:

- **step 1** ○ build a safety culture
- **step 2** ○ lead and support your staff
- **step 3** ○ integrate your risk management activity
- **step 4** ○ promote reporting
- **step 5** ○ involve and communicate with patients and the public

▷ **step 6** ○ learn and share safety lessons
▷ **step 7** ○ implement solutions to prevent harm.

These steps echo good practice in clinical governance but allow the smaller parts of the huge system that is the NHS to feed back to the top, enabling better dissemination of guidance and collection of data. They have identified a 'fishbone diagram' that can be used to analyse events in what they term 'Root Cause Analysis' but could also be used very easily in Significant Event Analysis (Figure 4.3). The problem to be explored is analysed according to each category or 'bone' along the spine, in order to look at the problem from a system as well as an individual point of view.

Figure 4.3 ○ ***Fishbone diagram from NPSA toolkit***

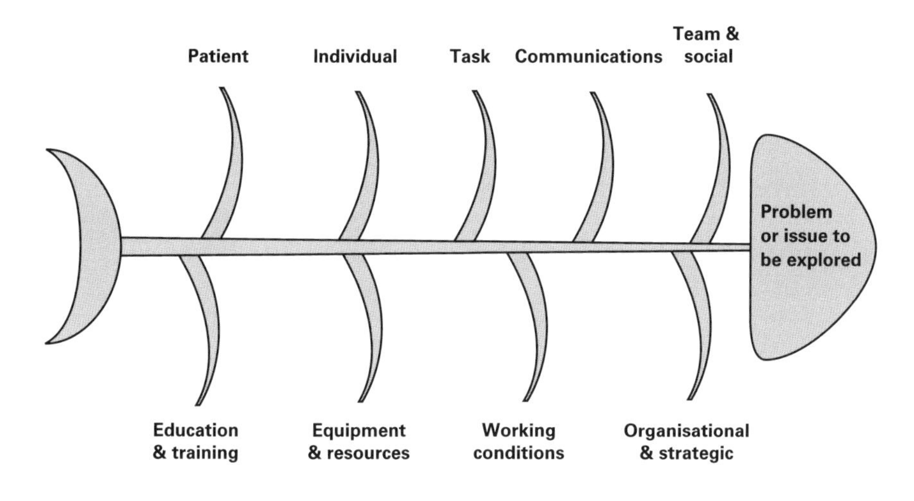


*Source*: National Patient Safety Agency.[17] Reproduced with permission from the National Patient Safety Agency.

## The appraisal system

This was introduced in 1998 as part of a consultation document *A First Class Service* and then further refined in *Supporting Doctors, Protecting Patients.*[18] Appraisal was described as:

> *a positive process to give someone feedback on their performance, to chart their continuing progress and to identify development needs. It is a forward looking process.*

Appraisal for GPs became a contractual requirement in 2002, a year after consultants. The original plan was that every doctor had an appraisal and that every five years the information about this would be collected together to provide evidence for revalidation. Current changes in legislation have paved the way for revalidation to occur. In 2008 the GMC is starting to ensure that all doctors who actively practise medicine hold a *licence,* to distinguish them from doctors registered with the GMC who do not practise.

Appraisal is now carried out yearly for all doctors, and is a formative process, designed to aid reflection, plan future development and enhance patient care.

As part of the appraisal every doctor will collect information against the statement of *Good Medical Practice,* available as electronic documents. The evidence in the folder will then be reviewed and discussed with a peer, an appraiser who will develop a PDP with the doctor and mutually agree comments that are filled in as part of a Form 4, held by the PCT. The overall structure is the same whether for a doctor in training or an established GP. *Good Medical Practice* sets out the principles and values on which good practice is founded; these principles together describe medical professionalism in action. The guidance is addressed to doctors, but is also intended for the public.[19] The guidance is further expanded for GPs explaining what a good doctor would do against these standards. In essence the guidance on appraisal states that:

- the appraiser should be another GP (or educational supervisor in the case of doctors in training), who will have been properly trained in carrying out appraisal
- appraisee and appraiser should prepare by identifying issues to discuss in the appraisal discussion, and reflecting on them
- the assessment of some of the more specialist aspects of a GP's clinical performance should be carried out by peers who are fully acquainted with the relevant areas of expertise and knowledge
- there should be clearly agreed local procedures for resolving individual concerns about appraisal that fit within the national model
- the appraisal should conclude by setting down, as an action plan, the agreements that have been reached about what each party is committed to doing. This should include the essentials of the PDP.

  Key development objectives for the following year and subsequent years should be set out in the PDP.

Appraisal documents for all doctors have the same format. The content of the accompanying text and portfolio evidence would reflect the individual doctor, his or her role and current activity:

- **form 1** ○ personal details
- **form 2** ○ current medical activities
- **form 3** ○ material for appraisal that should include reflective and portfolio evidence against the GMC standards of:
  - good clinical care
  - maintaining good medical practice
  - relationships with patients (to include patient feedback, peer review, significant events, complaint reviews)
  - working with colleagues
  - teaching and training
  - probity
  - management activity
  - research
  - health
- **form 4** ○ summary of findings.



---

## Continuing Professional Development

At the time of writing the principles underlying Continuing Professional Development (CPD) are being re-evaluated. The RCGP proposes a national, managed CPD scheme for GPs to support educational and professional development. The discussion document is available to read at www.rcgp.org.uk/docs/cpd_strategy_good_gps.doc. The essence of its scheme includes a proposal for 50 'credits' worth of learning a year, bringing GPs into line with other doctors and guidance from the other royal colleges. Its also states that the proposed scheme should:

- support the diversity and flexibility of general practice
- include a recognition of a range of learning styles
- be acceptable to employed and self-employed GPs
- focus on the need to support core general practice as described in the GP curriculum
- standardise the role and functions of GP educationalists across the UK
- be based around appraisal and provide guidance on PDPs.

It is likely that throughout 2008 and beyond further guidance will develop and GPs are encouraged to look at the RCGP website (www.rcgp.org.uk) for guidance.

### Revalidation, relicensure and recertification

The Chief Medical Officer was asked to carry out a review of issues arising from Dame Janet Smith's report *Safeguarding Patients*.[20] The report followed her inquiry into the events that lead up to Harold Shipman murdering up to 250 people. *Safeguarding Patients* had the aim of setting things in place to enable the NHS to prevent such a thing happening again. The report made 109 recommendations covering:

- ▷ the constitution of the GMC and its disciplinary procedures
- ▷ handling complaints and whistleblowing
- ▷ clinical governance, revalidation and appraisal
- ▷ monitoring general practitioners and the role of the PCTs.

An initial consultation was carried out and resulted in the report *Good Doctors, Safer Patients*,[21] which in turn was instrumental in influencing the white paper *Trust, Assurance and Safety*.[22] In the report Professor Sir Liam Donaldson explains his research, which shows that the public assumes that doctors are checked for their knowledge and competence regularly. He acknowledges that primary care presents a particularly difficult problem in identifying poor performance, as PCTs have only very limited access to information. His report suggests that appraisal should be developed further to be a more rigorous and summative exercise than the softer, formative procedure it currently is. The report indicates that revalidation is replaced by *relicensure and recertification*. The former relates to the renewal of full registration and the latter to the renewal of the doctor's specialist recertification. He also makes a link to the role of medical school, quoting research showing that over a quarter of risked disciplinary action in a doctor's career could be attributed to prior unprofessional behaviour in medical school.[23] Among his many other proposals picked up by the white paper was the development of GMC affiliates, individuals who take responsibility for the recognition and investigation of performance at a more local level.

Future proposals on revalidation are likely to be based on these principles:

- ▷ revalidation needs to be built upon enhanced systems of local clinical governance and appraisal
- ▷ the implementation needs to be phased, and carefully piloted
- ▷ revalidation should be approached as a single set of outcomes: relicensing for all doctors and for those on the GMC's specialist and GP registers; *recertification*. In turn recertification needs to be rooted in the evidence of actual performance
- ▷ that the activities of professional regulation needs to be linked with

systems-based regulation (e.g. by the Healthcare Commission in England), so as to maximise effectiveness and minimise the regulatory burdens for doctors, employers and other healthcare providers (source: www.gmc-uk.org/publications/gmc_today/March_2008_GMCtoday.pdf).

---

## The National Clinical Assessment Service

The National Clinical Assessment Authority (NCAS) was set up as a special health authority in 2001, as a response to the government document *Supporting Doctors, Protecting Patients*.[18] It became the National Clinical Assessment Service in 2005, and is now part of the NPSA. It describes itself as a 'Confidential support to the health service in managing practitioners whose performance gives cause for concern.'[24] It acts as an advisory service for doctors and dentists, working closely with the NPSA, the Academy of Medical Royal Colleges, the GMC, General Dental Council, the Healthcare Commission, and postgraduate deaneries. The NCAS describes its activities as:



- ▷ responding to requests for help by an employer or contracting organisation, and then assessing the practitioner
- ▷ providing educational support to NHS organisations for local management of performance concerns, in particular on the early detection of problems
- ▷ developing an expertise in evaluation, research and development.

The vast majority of those contacting the service are senior members of NHS organisations, such as clinical governance leads and senior executives. However, it does occasionally take direct referrals from individuals who perceive themselves to be at risk of performance problems or from 'whistle-blowers' (these are individuals who perceive performance putting patients at risk and who feel that the system is not acting on the problem). Once a problem has been identified the NCAS will meet with the employing or contracting body (in the case of GPs this will usually be the PCT). A problem that presents a serious risk to patients will be referred straight to the GMC. Those that are less clear will be assessed in three ways:

1 ▷ an assessment by an NCAS-approved occupational health physician to exclude any health problems as a major contributing problem
2 ▷ behavioural assessment by an occupational health psychologist
3 ▷ on-site clinical assessment (2–3 days), with a report covering the performance with reference to *Good Medical Practice*.

Once these measures have been undertaken a meeting between the GP and the PCT will occur, and a structured action plan will be agreed. For a GP the PCT will work with the practice to ensure appropriate support is put in place whilst the educational action plan is in operation. It is worth noting that a PCT might help financially, but it is likely that both the practice and the individual will have to bear some of the costs themselves. In the case of locum GPs the NCAS will determine who the responsible employing/contracting body is at the outset. (It might be that the PCT holds details of the locum on its performer list or occasionally the PCT responsible for referral.)

---

### Reporting poor performance

If you suspect a fellow healthcare professional of having performance problems that are putting patients at risk:



1 ▷ make sure you have your facts correctly
2 ▷ if you are unsure talk to a trusted colleague (your trainer if you are a registrar, the secretary of the British Medical Association (BMA) Local Medical Committee (LMC), the clinical governance lead in the practice or the PCT)
3 ▷ decide whether the patient risk is so high that a referral to the GMC is needed (you are able to telephone them for advice); you might also wish to speak to your defence union
4 ▷ the practitioner concerned will need to be informed, and you might wish to consider how this is best done and by whom, and whether following your discussion the individual will be able to continue working. He or she might wish to consult the defence union, and the LMC secretary or mentor
5 ▷ the PCT clinical governance lead should then be informed (in the case of a doctor in training the deanery should be informed, often via the area director). The PCT clinical governance lead will then decide on whether an immediate GMC referral and suspension is required (and might consult with the NCAS). Each PCT will have a Performance Panel (sometimes called a Poorly Performing Doctors Panel) that will meet to review the case confidentially. The outcome of the discussion, which might involve further fact-finding, will be:
   - nothing, in the case of a one-off problem, or an example where the individual and the practice have appropriately looked into and rectified the system
   - further support to the individual and the practice to help prevent any further deterioration in performance
   - referral to the GMC with support for the practice discussed, and

suspension from the PCT performer list if necessary
- referral to the NCAS, with an agreement of the supporting measures the PCT should put in place once the NCAS action plan has been received.

In the case of other healthcare professionals, the clinical governance lead at the PCT will be able to advise practices or individuals for the correct regulatory path for non-medical healthcare professionals.

## Conclusion

The vast majority of GPs practise well and safely for the whole of their professional lives. Safe practice is best in a practice or organisation with a supportive and positive culture that facilitates developing as part of a learning organisation. The NHS has also developed procedures for identifying performance problems and helping doctors in difficulty, ideally before patients are put at risk.



## Questions

**1** ▷ When was clinical governance introduced into the NHS?

**2** ▷ How does clinical governance work in a practice?

**3** ▷ What is the role of the PCT in clinical governance?

**4** ▷ What is a doctor's performance measured against?

**5** ▷ What is the NCAS?

**6** ▷ What three processes take place when a doctor is assessed by the NCAS?

**7** ▷ Who can refer to the NCAS?

**8** ▷ What should you do if you suspect a colleague of putting patients at risk?

**9** ▷ Who is responsible for paying for a doctor to be 'retrained' following an NCAS assessment?

**10** ▷ What are the current CPD arrangements for GPs?

## References


1 • Department of Health. *An Organisation with a Memory: report of an expert group on learning from adverse events in the NHS* London: The Stationery Office, 2000.

2 • Smith R. All changed, utterly changed *British Medical Journal* 1998; **316**: 1917–18.

3 • Scally G, Donaldson L. Looking forward: clinical governance and the drive for quality improvement in the new NHS in England *British Medical Journal* 1998; **317**: 61–5.

4 • *Report of the Committee on the Financial Aspects of Corporate Governance* London: Gee, 1992.

5 • Lilley R. *Making Sense of Clinical Governance* Oxford: Radcliffe Medical Press, 1999.

6 • Royal College of General Practitioners. *Clinical Governance* [curriculum statement 3.1], 2007, www.rcgp-curriculum.org.uk/PDF/curr_3_1_Clinical_Governance.pdf [accessed September 2008].

7 • National Audit Office. *Clinical Audit in England*, in *HC27 Session 1995–96* London: NAO, 1995.

8 • Wall D, Gerada C, Conlon M, *et al.* Supporting clinical governance in primary care *Clinical Governance: An International Journal* 2006; **11(1)**: 30–8.

9 • Leap LL. Striving for perfection *Clinical Chemistry* 2002; **48(11)**: 1871–2.

10 • Chambers R, Boath E. *Clinical Governance and Clinical Effectiveness Made Easy* Oxford: Radcliffe Medical Press, 1998.

11 • Department of Health. *Integrated Governance Handbook*, 2006, www.dh.gov.uk/en/Publicationsandstatistics/Publications/PublicationsPolicyAndGuidance/DH_4128739 [accessed September 2008].

12 • Department of Health. *Corporate Governance in the NHS, Code of Conduct, Code of Accountability* London: The Stationery Office, 1994.

13 • McSherry R, Pearce P. *Clinical Governance: a guide to implementation for healthcare professionals* Oxford: Blackwell Science, 2002.

14 • Royal College of General Practitioners. *Patient Safety* [curriculum statement 3.2], 2007, www.rcgp-curriculum.org.uk/PDF/curr_3_2_Patient_safety.pdf [accessed September 2008].

15 • National Patient Safety Agency. *Being Open Policy*, www.npsa.nhs.uk [accessed September 2008], 2005.

16 • Department of Health and National Patient Safety Agency. *Seven Steps to Patient Safety for Primary Care* London: NPSA, 2006.

17 • National Patient Safety Agency. www.msnpsa.nhs.uk.rcatoolkit/course/iindex.htm [accessed September 2008].

18 • Department of Health. *Supporting Doctors, Protecting Patients* London: DoH, 1999.

19 • General Medical Council. *Good Medical Practice: a guide for doctors* London: GMC, 2006.

20 • Smith J. *Safeguarding Patients: lessons from the past – proposals for the future* [The Shipman Inquiry] London: The Stationery Office, 2004.

21 • Department of Health. *Good Doctors, Safer Patients: proposals to strengthen the system to assure and improve the performance of doctors and to protect the safety of patients* London: The Stationery Office, 2006.

22 • The Secretary of State for Health. *Trust, Assurance and Safety: the regulation of health professionals in the 21st Century* London: The Stationery Office, 2007.

23 • Papadakis M A, Teherani A, Banach M A, *et al.* Disciplinary action by medical boards and prior behaviour in medical school *New England Journal of Medicine* 2005; **353**: 2673–82.

24 • National Clinical Assessment Service. *National Clinical Assessment Service Handbook,* 2007, www.ncas.npsa.nhs.uk/resources/publications/key-publications [accessed September 2008].

# The primary healthcare team

# 5

*Jim Waits*

## *Scenario*

*You have just started as a registrar at a practice. You have had a discussion with district nurses who are frustrated that they have not been able to replace a nurse who has left because of a 'freezing' of posts at the PCT. You are surprised that the district nurses are not employed in the practice.*

*You discuss this with your trainer who suggests you have a look at all those who interact with the practice to provide care and to find out who is employed and managed by whom. He also asks you to think about whether it is important where the contracts of employment are held or not.*



## Introduction

This chapter looks at the primary healthcare team (PHCT). It focuses mainly on those that are employed by, or based in, the practice and those that work directly with GPs in their locality. There are many other healthcare individuals who will be working in primary care (PCT public health teams, dentists, ophthalmic services, health promotion). The chapter will also outline:

- ▷ the difference between practice-employed staff and practice-based team members
- ▷ the role of the PHCT
- ▷ the work roles of the members of the team
- ▷ their team roles
- ▷ the contribution the team members make to clinical governance.

Issues relating directly to employment are discussed in Chapter 7.

## Practice-employed staff and practice-based staff

The point is made elsewhere that partners are not employees, either of the NHS or in the practice. The clinical employees of the practice generally include:

- salaried (or associate) doctors. This category includes registrars, specialist training grade and Foundation Year 2 doctors, as well as those doctors who are employed by the practice and receive a salary (unlike partners, who have a profit share)
- practice nurses
- nurse practitioners (nurses with an extended role who might provide clinical services traditionally provided by other members of the healthcare team)
- healthcare assistants and/or phlebotomists
- managerial and administrative staff
- receptionists
- cleaners
- other clinical staff, which will vary according to the practice and the local services provided by the PCT, including those working on new services provided by the practice under Practice-Based Commissioning (PBC) (see Chapter 3). These might include counsellors, diabetes specialist nurses, dieticians, health visitors with special remits, drug and alcohol workers, etc.
- other clinical staff and non-NHS professional staff, who play a valuable role in supporting the patients. Usually they are employees of the Primary Care Organisation (PCO) or the local authority, or increasingly in some areas might be employed by a private firm that has successfully bid to provide a particular clinical service to patients in the locality. These might be practice-based (i.e. working from practice premises, often with access to the GP records) or might work from another location. They link into the practice by providing services to the practice population in the community. They include (and this list is not exhaustive) the following (the staff who are often practice-based are marked with an asterisk *):
  - midwives,* who are often employed by a hospital trust
  - health visitors*
  - district nurses*
  - social workers*
  - physiotherapists
  - occupational therapists
  - pharmacist/PCO pharmaceutical adviser (very often employed by the PCO and providing support for a certain number of hours a week)
  - other 'attached staff' might include benefits advisers, employment rehabilitation, palliative care nursing staff, or diabetes specialist nurses, often reflecting the particular needs of the local population or the relative distance from secondary care services.

Various funding initiatives (see Chapters 1 and 3) have led to an increase in practice-employed staff, most commonly, for example, physiotherapists. The development of PBC could radically change the employment arrangements for many practice-based staff as practices investigate the opportunity to improve the accessibility of services where waiting times are regarded as unacceptable under the existing arrangements or there is an under-provision of patients' services in the locality.

The employment arrangements for this clinical group, when looking at the care of patients, is irrelevant provided:

- members of the PHCT are focused on the need of individual patients
- communications are effective between those employed in the practice and those based in, or providing a service to, the practice
- records are shared
- management of staff time is allocated according to the practice population.



## The role of the primary healthcare team

It is important to realise that effective working is not reliant on formal meetings. Undoubtedly the PHCT should meet on a regular basis with an agenda and formal minutes to record agreements and action (see Chapter 9). The agenda often focuses on general principles and concerns, e.g. the impact of staff shortages, but might be centred around an individual patient's care. The latter could come from a formal multidisciplinary meeting to discuss significant or critical events (see Chapter 4), to highlight an example of good practice, or to discuss the expansion or contraction of a team. The scenario highlights the need to review the size and nature of the PHCT as both the population and the funding of primary care changes.

However, patients' needs will arise and change from day to day and it is important that members of the team establish an effective means of communication, both formal and informal, to fulfil those needs, which can begin before birth and continue to the end of life. For example, health visitors and social workers might be the first to know that a child might need protection even before it is born and it is essential that this information is properly recorded in practice records; they will need to communicate with the GP, midwife and outside agencies in child protection, as well as hospital maternity services.

Towards the end of life district nurses might be the first to know that a patient has been discharged from hospital and is expected to die at home.

The doctors of the practice might rely on the nurses communicating this information to them so that they can provide appropriate medical support.

Under the provisions of the Quality and Outcomes Framework (QoF) practices are set standards for clinical and non-clinical activity. The achievement of the standards is rewarded by extra money for the time and effort put into managing the recording and communication of data. For example:

▷ **Management 1** ○ requires that individual healthcare professionals have access to information on local procedures relating to child protection
▷ where patients are dying at home **Records 13** of the contract requires that there is a system to alert the out-of-hours service or duty doctor to patients dying at home
▷ **Palliative Care 2** ○ requires regular (at least three monthly) multidisciplinary case review meetings where all patients on the palliative care register are discussed.



*These examples serve to highlight the fact that the GMS2 contract is about providing a high quality of services to patients, and effective communications between all healthcare professionals are fundamental to that objective.*

---

## The role of doctors in the primary healthcare team

### *Partners*

The term partner is a legal one used in the Partnership Act 1890 and other legislation to define those who own a business. Partners are not paid salaries but rely on a profitable business for their income; the higher the income and/or the lower the expenses the greater the profit. A partnership should have a formal agreement for which legal advice is required. The Partnership Act applies in the absence of an agreement or if the agreement fails to specify how particular requirements of the act are to be decided. For example, the partners are deemed to have an equal share of the profits unless the agreement specifies otherwise; this is obviously necessary if a partner is less than full-time while others are full-time.

In law partners are jointly and severally liable for the acts or decisions of any one of them in relation to the business. For example, a partner could order an item of equipment for the practice without the agreement of the other partners and the cost of the equipment would fall on the practice regardless of the opinion of the other partners. Normally a partnership agreement would require a majority or unanimous decision for expenditure in excess of an agreed amount to ensure that no one partner could commit the practice in this way.

It is not usual to find a limited-liability partnership in general practice though they are being introduced as a vehicle for joint ventures with private companies to support Practice-Based Commissioning. The Limited Liability Partnership Act 2000 applies to this form of partnership.

Partners should play a pivotal role in defining the clinical and patient-focused ethos of a practice. This will be generated by an enthusiasm for a high quality of patient services, whether that is:

- the first face-to-face contact by a potential patient who approaches the practice administrative staff
- the commitment to a range of appointment times to suit patients
- a readiness to be available for telephone consultations, etc.

A practice where the partners demonstrate these non-clinical commitments to patients will almost certainly be one where clinical staff are encouraged to work to high professional standards and administrative staff are rewarded for being courteous and helpful.

One of the partners will often chair or take part in PHCT meetings, making sure that the practice partnership meetings are kept up to date with issues and the PHCT kept abreast of practice-based changes.

One of the partners or the practice manager will usually have lead responsibility as Caldicott Guardian. Caldicott Guardians are senior staff in the NHS and social services appointed to protect patient information. The 1997 *Report of the Review of Patient-Identifiable Information*, chaired by Dame Fiona Caldicott (the Caldicott report), made a number of recommendations for regulating the use and transfer of patient-identifiable information between NHS organisations in England and to non-NHS bodies. The aim was to ensure that patient-identifiable information was shared only for justified purposes and that only the minimum necessary information was shared in each case. The Department of Health (DoH) manual for Caldicott Guardians can be found at www.dh.gov.uk/en/Publicationsandstatistics/Publications/PublicationsPolicyAndGuidance/DH_062722.

### Salaried doctors

A salaried doctor is an employee of the practice and is not a partner. Even salaried partners must not, in law, be interpreted as taking part in partnership decisions.

As for all other employees the salaried doctor will have a contract of employment and a job description/job plan. He or she will enjoy all the benefits of the extensive employment law, including protection against discrimination, unfair dismissal, etc., and be subject to the provisions of the practice policies on staff matters.

For salaried doctors in General Medical Services (GMS) practices and PCOs, the General Practitioners Committee (GPC) Model Contract revised in August 2007 must be used as the basis for the contract of employment (see www.bma.org.uk/ap.nsf/Content/FocusSalariedGps0604). Personal Medical Services (PMS) practices are encouraged to adopt the Model Contract but are not obliged to do so.

The duties of the salaried doctor will have been set out in a job description/ job plan at the time the post was advertised and subsequently be agreed at the time of his or her appointment.

The GPC guidance for the preparation of a job plan, issued in November 2005, can be found at www.bma.org.uk/ap.nsf/Content/jobplannov05 and in summary includes the advice that:



> *Job Plans should be developed collaboratively between the employer and employee. They should be revised only by mutual agreement. This should be done at a minimum of 8–12 weeks after initial appointment, and then annually, or when there are any significant changes to the work pattern suggested by either party.*

The guidance suggests that:

***1 ▷ Scheduling in a job plan should include:***

*a) Clinical duties*
*b) Administration/paperwork*
*c) Primary care team meetings*
*d) Personal CPD (continuing professional development) time*
*e) Time for personal mentoring*
*f) Specific specialist roles in the practice*

***2 ▷ Workload should be:***

*(a) Defined in amount (number of patients) and type (clinical, paperwork, team meetings), with provisions for fluctuations in exceptional circumstances*
*(b) Reflect the individual employee's particular abilities and developmental priorities*
*(c) Realistically match contracted hours as defined in the contract of employment*
*(d) Balanced, recognising both clinical and non-clinical work*

***3 ▷ Extra contractual duties: there must be clear agreement on arrangements regarding how and when extra-contractual duties will be recognized***

***4 ▷ Session length: although a session is defined as 4 hours and 10 minutes, periods of duty do not need to be exact multiples of sessions***

***5 ▷ EWTD: breaks should be granted within worked hours in keeping with the European Working Time Directive***

6 ▷ ***Improving working lives: start and finish times should consider the employee's need to meet childcare or other care commitments***
7 ▷ ***Paperwork***
8 ▷ ***On-call commitment should be specified***
9 ▷ ***Clinical workload***
10 ▷ ***Assessment of workload***
11 ▷ ***Surgery times***
12 ▷ ***Visits***

The guidance also has 'Commonly asked questions', an outline job plan, suggested 'Coding activities for a diary' and an outline diary.

Usually a salaried doctor will be encouraged to develop his or her own patient following and a number of routine appointments included in the normal work pattern for this. Increasingly, salaried doctors are seeing patients who seek medical assistance on the day, variously called duty, emergency or triage patients, either for part of the day or a full day.

Some salaried doctors (sometimes called associates) will develop lead roles in a particular specialty and more managerial roles, often under the mentorship of a more experienced partner, in order to gain experience prior to applying for a partnership role elsewhere.

Salaried doctors are often managerially accountable to the practice manager, e.g. to agree annual leave dates. Annual appraisals would normally be undertaken with a partner since this is an opportunity to discuss clinical matters, possible career development, etc.

Salaried doctors should also bear in mind that they can approach the Local Medical Committee (LMC) for impartial and confidential advice.

### *Specialty registrars and Foundation Year 2 doctors*

These are doctors in training and will be supervised by a named trainer (another doctor) in the practice. The training contract with the practice will specify the particular needs to be fulfilled during their time in the practice. The trainee will have protected time with his or her tutor and/or other mentor each week as part of that contract. If time permits the trainee should have a tutorial with the practice manager and senior practice nurse, particularly if the trainee aspires to become a partner.

The Royal College of General Practitioners (RCGP) is developing a web-based resource for registrars. At the time of writing the relevant pages were at the development stage but can be found at www.rcgp.org.uk/default.aspx?page=5439.

Trainees might find it useful to access the RCGP 'brief guide to clinical supervisors' at www.rcgp-curriculum.org.uk/pdf/curr_Brief%20guide%20for%20clinical%20supervisors%20aug07.pdf, which will provide some insight into the College's expectations of the training and support their tutor is expected to provide.

It is important that trainees seeks whatever assistance they require not only from the doctors but also from nursing and administrative staff, e.g. arranging appointment times that are long enough to enable trainees to have confidence in the diagnosis and treatment of the patient.

They might, as part of their learning needs, have identified an audit, most often looking at an area where clinical activity can be improved. It is vital that, where relevant, all PHCT members can be involved, thus reflecting the importance of the team in managing patients in primary care. When the results are submitted to the PHCT all the clinical members can discuss how to introduce the outcomes of the audit for the benefit of patients.



## Employed staff

The following sections describe the roles, duties and responsibilities of staff employed in practices. Many practice managers will subscribe to First Practice Management (www.firstpracticemanagement.co.uk), which has an extensive library of more detailed draft job descriptions for these staff in the members' section of the website.

### *Nursing staff*

These generally fall into two groups:

- those *employed by the practice* and based in the practice, most commonly as 'practice nurses' and healthcare assistants/phlebotomists
- those employed by the PCO (e.g. district nurses, health visitors, intermediate care nurses) that work in the community.

Although there might be a great deal of overlap in their skills the two groups of nurses have duties that inevitably mean that they work largely in isolation from one another. It is essential to encourage good communication between nurses employed in the practice and between practices and with nurses working in the community, if this isolation is not to hinder professional development, or to reduce the care provided to patients. Nurses have a personal responsibility to ensure that they fulfil the requirements of their professional body, the Nursing and Midwifery Council (www.nmc-uk.org), to adhere to the Code of Conduct and undertake Continuing Professional Development (Post-Registration Education and Practice [PREP]). Practices should respect that requirement and allow time for study leave.

There might be a *senior practice nurse or nursing team lead* who is responsible for managing and supporting all other practice nurses employed in the practice, although this role will often be dependent on the size of the practice. Ideally his or her role will include:

- ▷ providing leadership to the practice nurse team, in collaboration with the general practitioners and the practice manager, to develop an effective, high-quality nursing service
- ▷ promoting integrated nursing practice within the wider nursing team (practice nurses, district nurses and health visitors) underpinned by the development of evidence-based practice guidelines, for shared delivery of care to the patients of the practice
- ▷ ensuring that relevant protocols are produced, revised regularly and used appropriately
- ▷ liaising with the PCO and his or her senior practice nurse counterparts in other practices to discuss professional nursing matters.

The detailed job description for a senior practice nurse can be extensive and demanding, and will change according to the size and nature of the general practice.

Increasingly practices are wishing to extend the role of healthcare assistants (see pp. 68–9) and the senior nurse will take the lead in identifying clinical duties that can be undertaken by an unqualified but appropriately trained and supported nurse. These duties will be transferred from the registered nurses to allow them to undertake, for example, nurse-led clinics that could relieve GPs of some clinical commitments.

The senior practice nurse will almost certainly undertake hands-on clinical duties as well as providing support to other nurses in the practice.

*Nurse practitioners* have advanced nursing skills and increasingly are able to prescribe and have a valuable role to play in a practice. As nurse prescribers they are able to fulfil some routine consultations that would otherwise require a GP appointment. Nurse practitioners are often part of and are managed in the nursing team, but might also be managed as part of the medical team in some cases.

The nurse practitioner's role could include:

- ▷ triage of patients
- ▷ diagnosis and treatment of minor illness, including the issue of prescriptions for a limited range of medications

- referral to secondary care, in consultation with a GP
- provision of continuing care for patients with chronic illness
- healthcare promotion.

Some or all of these duties might be offered in branch surgeries, pharmacies, or other locations remote from the main surgery.

In the PHCT they have a particular role in sharing their expertise to help enhance the skills of other professional staff.

*Practice nurses* (registered nurses) employed by the practice will offer a range of skills including:

- nurse-led clinics for asthma, COPD, diabetes, etc. to fulfil the requirements of the QoF contract
- participation in minor treatments with the GP
- joint injections
- cervical smears
- dressings of varying complexity
- pulse neuropathy for diabetic patients
- childhood immunisations
- travel vaccination advice and injections
- new patient consultation
- smoking cessation clinics, weight management clinics
- ear-syringing
- blood tests, etc.

The nurses normally work to practice protocols for these services, which should be reviewed at least annually.

It would be unusual for any one nurse to be competent to offer all the services outlined above. Many practice nurses have specialist diplomas that are now offered for asthma, family planning, etc.

One of the practice nurses or the senior practice nurse will carry lead responsibility for the maintenance of the Controlled Drugs Register, ensuring that all deliveries are recorded immediately and stock-checked on a weekly basis.

A *healthcare assistant* (HCA) is a nurse who has not had formal nursing training, but might have undertaken a vocational NVQ qualification. Their work is much more supervised and duties include:

- new patient consultation
- ear-syringing
- blood taking
- smoking cessation clinics
- minor dressings, etc.

Many practices have sought to extend the role of the HCA and some initiatives have been controversial, such as administering influenza vaccinations (under a Patient-Specific Direction).

It is essential that HCAs have appropriate training and support if they are to assume duties previously assigned to registered nurses. Effective communication is also essential in the practice so that everyone involved can understand that time freed from tasks as above will allow registered nurses to take a clinical lead in new areas.

Those interested in the initiatives being explored nationally should look at the information available at the Working in Partnership Programme website (www.wipp.nhs.uk).

*Phlebotomists* are generally limited to blood-taking. They might be part of the receptionist team or be HCAs. In some areas phlebotomists employed by a practice will visit patients in their own home, while in others the phlebotomy service is one provided by the PCO as part of the District Nursing Service. Again there are specific courses and training requirements to ensure safe practice.



### Practice-based nurses

*Community matrons* have been appointed in some areas as a recent innovation by the DoH. They are usually employed by the PCO and might provide a service to one or more practices. Not all practices benefit from having access to a community matron. The DoH describes the role of the community matron as follows:

> The NHS Improvement Plan *(2004) described a new clinical role for nurses. Known as community matrons, these experienced, skilled nurses use case management techniques with patients who meet a criteria* [sic] *denoting very high intensity use of health care. With special intensive help, these patients are able to remain at home longer and to have more choice about their health care.*
>
> *The case management work of community matrons is central to the government's policy for the management of people with long term conditions.*
>
> *In this type of case management, community matrons:*
>
> - *use data to actively seek out patients who will benefit*
> - *combine high level assessment of physical, mental and social care needs*
> - *review medication and prescribe medicines via independent and supplementary prescribing arrangements*
> - *provide clinical care and health promoting interventions*
> - *co-ordinate inputs from all other agencies, ensuring all needs are met*
> - *teach and educate patients and their carers about warning signs of*

*complications or crisis*
- *provide information so patients and families can make choices about current and future care needs*
- *are highly visible to patients and their families and carers, and are seen by them as being in charge of their care*
- *are seen by colleagues across all agencies as having the key role for patients with very high intensity needs.*

The DoH also offers this expectation of the outcomes:

*Case management by community matrons will:*

- *help to prevent unnecessary admissions to hospital*
- *reduce length of stay of necessary hospital admissions*
- *improve outcomes for patients*
- *integrate all elements of care*
- *improve patients' ability to function and their quality of life*
- *help patients and their families plan for the future*
- *increase choice for patients*
- *enable patients to remain in their homes and communities*
- *improve end of life care*

(www.dh.gov.uk/en/Longtermconditions/DH_4134132).

*Community midwives* are usually employed by the Acute Hospitals Trust and might be practice-based for part of each week. Midwives have assumed many of the clinical responsibilities previously undertaken by GPs. Whilst most GPs have welcomed this initiative it is important that any patient's potential antenatal and postnatal problem is recorded in the patient's records, and in serious cases brought to the attention of the patient's usual GP. GPs will still be responsible for managing any emergencies that present to them and providing medical support throughout the pregnancy for conditions not managed by the midwives or obstetricians.

*Health visitors* are usually employed by the PCO and might be based in the practice. Health visitors contend that they are unusual among health professions in that they focus on health and wellbeing rather than disease or illness, and they identify recognised and unrecognised health needs.

All families with a child under five have a named health visitor or health visiting team who can advise on all aspects of care, for example:

- feeding
- behaviour
- immunisation
- parenting

- ▷ sleeping
- ▷ teething
- ▷ special needs, etc.

Health visitors also support the whole family and can help with:

- ▷ benefits
- ▷ childcare options
- ▷ employment
- ▷ home safety
- ▷ local support groups and leisure activities
- ▷ role of fathers
- ▷ support for single parents and with parenting
- ▷ addressing conflicts within the family and domestic violence, etc.

Health visitors also refer to other agencies for specialist help with problems such as bereavement, disability, unemployment, housing and homelessness, mental health (including postnatal depression).

Some health visitors run health promotion groups and clinics such as child health, healthy eating, smoking cessation, parenting, etc.

Health visitors can also advise on:

- ▷ contraception
- ▷ depression
- ▷ disability
- ▷ isolation
- ▷ menopause
- ▷ pregnancy
- ▷ sexual health.

Health visitors contribute to the child protection process through referrals, attendance at case conferences and core groups; and as part of the child protection plan for individual children.

Health visitors liaise closely with other agencies in their communities, particularly with nurseries, playgroups and schools.

Most practices will have access to health visitors for the elderly, who will have a similar brief in looking at the health aspects but whose focus is obviously around the issues of ageing. They very often work in close collaboration with social services, community psychiatric nurses for the elderly and charities supporting elderly people in their own homes, such as Help the Aged.

*District nurses* are usually employed by the PCO and might be based in the practice. However, district nurses also have strong links with secondary care and most of the support they provide to patients in the community follows hospital discharge. They are also very involved with the nursing needs of the housebound patient and those who are terminally ill. District nurses usually know of a patient's discharge from hospital before the practice receives information from the hospital. Many of the roles and outcomes described above for community matrons fall within the remit of district nurses. District nurses have a wide range of roles that will often change widely according to the area in which they work. They might:

- assess patients
- plan and implement a care plan discussed with the patient
- fulfil necessary nursing procedures, e.g. injections, cannulae insertion, venepuncture, care of chemotherapy 'central' lines and parenteral feeding regimes
- work with social services and care agencies to support independent living
- provide support to those recently discharged, or those who are terminally ill.



*District nurses* work very closely with GPs, often providing the main care of those who are housebound, or requiring nursing in their own home as the end of life draws near. Many district nurses have additional skills and qualifications, enabling them to work with GPs and practice nurses in providing care and monitoring of the housebound in chronic diseases such as diabetes, coronary heart disease and certain lung diseases.

## The role of nurses in the primary healthcare team

Some patients require support from practice-employed nurses *and* practice-based nurses. Collectively they should:

- ensure that the services are effectively co-ordinated and offered in a timely fashion to meet the patient's needs
- maintain ongoing communication between all nurses involved in support of the patient
- update practice records promptly so that doctors and nurses in the practice are informed about the patient's condition and treatment, and particularly changes in these aspects of care
- bring any concerns to the attention of the doctor promptly
- reflect the needs of carers to professional staff in the practice or other statutory services.

There are many other nurses who might be involved in the PHCT, and this chapter cannot do justice to the range and skills of community nurses who might be trained in palliative care, community psychiatric nurses, diabetes specialist nurses, community drug and alcohol team members, and those nurses providing assessment and review of continence or outreach services from hospitals.

## Physiotherapists and occupational therapists, podiatrists

Traditionally community physiotherapy teams and occupational therapists worked from NHS-owned health centres or community hospitals. With the advent of funding changes in the 1990s (see Chapter 1) there are many more examples of physiotherapists in particular working from general practices. Most community physiotherapists will also work with the housebound, providing acute care for disabling musculoskeletal problems (e.g. acute back pain), chronic rehabilitation and support for those who have neuro-disabilities. Increasingly they provide *intermediate care* for patients in the community who would previously have been admitted to secondary care, or for patients who have been discharged much earlier from secondary care. As with the primary care nurses, good communication is vital to make the best of what is often a very stretched service.

Occupational therapists (OT) and podiatrists are less often found in general practices, most often working from PCO-based premises. They are also taking responsibility for an increased number of services, the OTs in particular working with secondary care and social services, as well as district nurses, physiotherapists, GPs and social services, to maintain individuals in their own home. Where these individuals are not in the same building as GPs and district nurses, their role and the need for good communication and inclusion in PHCT meetings should not be forgotten.

## Social workers, benefits advisers, Citizens Advice Bureaux and 'others'

Every locality will have different needs and projects. The needs of a very rural population in the north of Scotland against those in a deprived inner city will vary and so will the nature of the services provided within or alongside general practices. This chapter cannot do justice to all the professions and disciplines that may work within or alongside general practices, and as identified in the scenario it is important to get a good idea of who is out there, where they are based, and to find a way of including them.

*Managerial and administrative staff,* including receptionists, provide essential support to the clinicians in the practice.

*The practice manager* usually has a key role in the development of a modern practice as well as ensuring that all the usual management roles are fulfilled:

- **future planning** ○ identify potential developments in services, including national initiatives, and bring business cases for implementation to the attention of partners, e.g. PBC. Prepare a Business Continuity Plan for action in the event of a significant fire etc.
- **finance** ○ achieve practice profits within an agreed budget
- **QoF** ○ monitor achievements and highlight/take action necessary to achieve agreed targets
- **manage** all staff
- **patients' services** ○ respond to patients' concerns or complaints. Undertake annual patients' surveys. Review appointments arrangements regularly. Ensure patient confidentiality is respected by all staff
- **external liaison** with the PCO, practice accountant, solicitor, etc.
- **policies and protocols** ○ produce appropriate policies, e.g. staff sickness policy, and protocols, e.g. palliative care, and review regularly
- **legislation** ○ ensure that all legislative requirements are fulfilled relating to staff, health and safety, fire regulations, etc. (see Chapter 7)
- **IT** ○ oversee IT and other essential support services, including the training of staff
- **premises** ○ maintain premises with particular reference to security.



### Assistant practice manager

Larger practices will usually have one or more assistant practice managers with responsibility for some of the detailed duties outlined above. For example:

- preparation of the staff payroll
- payment of invoices and petty cash payments
- maintenance of the practice accounts on a day-to-day basis
- liaison with the practice accountant, bank staff, etc.
- supervision support and training of administrative and reception staff, including regular staff appraisals
- health and safety/fire risk assessments
- liaison with the clinical system company/PCO IT department
- patients' enquiries and complaints, liaising with clinical colleagues as appropriate

- preparation of the practice booklet and maintenance of the practice website and the NHS Choices website.

*Medical secretaries* provide a comprehensive audio and shorthand service to the partners and all staff. They:

- prepare referral and other letters
- submit urgent referrals
- liaise with secondary care, sending/taking messages for GPs
- open post and distribute it as appropriate
- collect statistics as required
- have a variable administration role, such as administering cervical screening or a flu vaccination programme
- undertake scanning of documents for attachment to the patients' records in the clinical system
- assist patients on Choose and Book.

Some practices are now using remote digital recording services for letter typing, leaving secretarial posts in the practice more free to perform other administrative tasks.

*Dispensing staff* are most commonly found in rural practices. They will be qualified to NVQ level 3 or 4 and will:

- issue medication prescribed by doctors or appropriate nurses
- collect prescription fees or ensure that free prescriptions are issued to those who qualify for them
- order replacement stock or new medication at the request of the doctors
- undertake stock checks at prescribed intervals. This will include a comprehensive stock-take at the end of the partnership financial year for the accountant
- maintain the practice formulary if required
- draw partners' attention to medication that is not being used.

Senior dispensing staff or the practice manager will meet representatives from the companies who supply the medication to negotiate prices for the purchases.

*Other administrative staff, including receptionists,* are often the first point of contact with patients and potential patients. They might work as one team covering all duties or be divided into sections for specific tasks:

- telephone duties include:
  - welcoming callers and transferring them as appropriate
  - arranging appointments for patients
  - advising patients of blood test and other test results, in accordance with clinicians' guidance

- ▷ printing repeat prescriptions and arranging for signature and subsequent collection
- ▷ welcoming patients who have appointments and guiding them to the relevant waiting area
- ▷ welcoming visitors
- ▷ helping new patients to complete forms as necessary
- ▷ arranging appointments as required
- ▷ ensuring that consultation rooms are checked each day and re-stocked with forms etc.
- ▷ pulling notes for patients' consultations and re-file the records
- ▷ filing
- ▷ scanning incoming documents, allocating Read codes as necessary
- ▷ contacting patients about childhood immunisations, smear tests due, etc.
- ▷ preparing the monthly return to the Prescription Pricing Authority
- ▷ preparing returns to the PCO as required.



*Cleaning staff* have an important, and often unrecognised, role in the practice. They help ensure that the premises appear clean and tidy to the patients, and thus provide a degree of reassurance to those who worry about infections acquired in a clinical environment.

They also have a critical part to play in infection control, provided an appropriate cleaning routine has been defined for them. For example, consultation room couches should be pulled out from a position against a wall on a regular basis and the wall and surrounding area cleaned thoroughly.

---

## The primary healthcare team and clinical governance

Clinical governance was described in Chapter 4. Clinical governance in terms of the PHCT:

- ▷ is the main vehicle for continuously improving the quality of patient care
- ▷ requires organisation-wide transformation, clinical leadership and positive organisational cultures
- ▷ enables the recognition and replication of good clinical practice to ensure that lessons are reliably learned from failures in standards of care.

However, most importantly clinical governance should be used to promote the introduction of improved clinical practice identified from innovative thinking in the practice, not necessarily related to failings in patient care. Professional staff of all clinical disciplines are thoughtful about the work they do and, by nature, seek improvements in standards. The PHCT can be the catalyst, and should certainly provide the opportunity, to highlight innovation and promote it for the benefit of patients. In some cases, however, the discussion at the PHCT meetings might have become routine and preoccupied with agenda items related more to staff's concerns about themselves rather than patients. This is likely to stem from the anxieties and uncertainties generated by national initiatives, e.g. Agenda for Change, or the cuts in staff having to be made by the PCO to balance the books.

If allowed to continue, the meeting might become routine or disruptive (see Chapter 9), and it is wise to consider initiatives to energise and enthuse the team.

One way of reinvigorating a moribund meeting would be to introduce innovation – include two items early on the agenda for each meeting:

- ▷ an audit of shortcomings in a patient's service or a particular clinical area, and ask different professional groups to find and report an example at successive meetings. An example of such a report might be a voluntary audit undertaken by a registrar or nurse in training. The purpose of discussing just one problem allows time to debate the issues properly and agree action for improvement. Care should be taken to look at areas in every PHCT members' remit and to avoid the perception of 'witch hunts'
- ▷ a clinical initiative to improve patients' services not yet introduced locally. The National Institute for Health and Clinical Excellence (NICE) guidelines can be a source of such an innovation, though doctors and nurses will identify many more from their reading of professional journals.

The PHCT might also find it useful to discuss:

- ▷ *QoF achievements* and the contribution that the multidisciplinary team can make to an improvement in patient care. It is too often assumed that the QoF is about financial reward to a practice when the true purpose is to demonstrate a measurable improvement in clinical standards, and to ensure the funds are there to continue to provide high-quality care
- ▷ *in-house changes* planned to improve services to patients, e.g. allowing patients to book appointments via the internet, better use of nursing and medical staff when looking at tissue viability, or palliative care

Improvements in patient care should be the *raison d'être* for every healthcare professional, and talking about improvements in a PHCT can be mentally refreshing and personally rewarding.

## Conclusion

Patients registered with one practice will have access to many members of the PHCT. Good communication and a positive culture can only enhance the care of those who are ill, vulnerable and housebound, and good integration of care should mean that patients receive the same standards of care irrespective of whether they are housebound or able to come to the surgery.

A good team should function well together irrespective of who employs the individuals, and an open and communicative practice is more likely to weather the storm of the increased number of healthcare providers that are being contracted to provide care in the community.



## Questions

**1** ▷ Why is communication important in the PHCT?

**2** ▷ What would you expect a community matron to achieve?

**3** ▷ What is different about the role of health visitors compared with other healthcare professionals?

**4** ▷ How would you extend the role of registered nurses without extra resources?

**5** ▷ What website offers information about extending the role of healthcare assistants?

**6** ▷ Partners should play a pivotal role in the practice – to achieve what?

**7** ▷ Why are salaried doctors valuable in a PHCT?

**8** ▷ How would you improve patient care through the PHCT?

**9** ▷ How would you disseminate a registrar's audit report to improve a service?

# The GP running a business

## What you need to know from your accountant

# 6

*Richard Lambert*

---

### *Scenario*

*You are a registrar who has just completed training, and who is now about to undertake locum GP work for the first time. You have never been anything other than a 'PAYE' or salaried employee and you want to make sure that you comply with necessary legislation when you commence your business.*

*You realise you need advice on the records that need to be kept, the tax system and how it impacts on the self-employed, and what forms need to be completed. You are also looking further ahead to the time when you might be offered a partnership and wish to find out what further matters should be taken into consideration at that time. In addition, you have heard that the rules concerning superannuation contributions have recently changed, and you are unsure as to how to make your contributions. You have made an appointment to see a specialist medical accountant to ask for advice.*

---

### Introduction

The above is typical of an initial meeting agenda between a newly qualified GP and an accountant. There is a lot to cover with such an agenda, and matters have to be kept relatively simple as the subject is so huge that an initial meeting cannot begin to cover all aspects. However, there are certain essentials that need to be covered to set the GP on the correct path so that they are confident that, come the year end, they will be in position to present their accounts and tax return information in a meaningful manner, and be guided through their first year confidently and without financial penalty. This chapter seeks to explain the key matters to be covered in broad outline, but there is not the space for a detailed examination, particularly of the taxation issues, and specialist advice should always be sought for individual circumstances. It goes without saying that a GP might well continue to be salaried by the practice; this scenario will have tax repercussions, which will inevitably be dependent on the individual, but is not covered specifically in this section.

## The GP as a locum

Becoming a locum is an inexorable move along the career path for a GP once the period as a registrar comes to an end. It also marks the entry into the world of self-employment. To someone whose only exposure to the world of tax and National Insurance (NI) has been the deductions on the monthly payslip, and perhaps the notice of needing a tax code (this is a code that is given by HM Revenue and Customs which will determine the amount of tax-free pay you have, and ultimately how much tax you will need to pay), it is a rude awakening. However, by following a few simple rules at the beginning will enable records to be kept that will allow accounts to be prepared and tax returns to be completed with the minimum of disruption.

### *Notification to HM Revenue and Customs*



One of the first matters to be dealt with is to notify HM Revenue and Customs (HMRC) that self-employment has commenced. There is a period of three full months from the end of the month in which self-employment commences to advise them of the fact, and there is a penalty for not doing so of £100 (penalties for not doing things on time are a recurrent theme in tax legislation). Notification is done on *form CWF1*, which can be downloaded from HMRC's vast and informative website (www.hmrc.gov.uk). This is the only notification that needs to be made as the form also covers registration for NI purposes.

### *National Insurance*

There are two classes of NI to be aware of:

**Class 2** ▷ which is paid on a weekly basis
**Class 4** ▷ which is profit-related (the NI deducted as an employee is Class 1).

The liability to Class 2 NI is triggered by the notification to HMRC above; it is at a level of £2.20 per week, and is paid monthly by direct debit. The Class 4 NI is paid when the self-employed tax liability is paid, and cannot be calculated until accounts are prepared. It is at a rate of 8 per cent on assessable profits between £5225 and £34,840, and 1 per cent on profits above £34,840 (figures quoted are for the 2007/08 tax year).

### Taxation

Taxation is covered in general terms later, but starting in business as a locum GP is likely to be the first time that the GP has to take responsibility for paying his or her own tax liabilities, as opposed to having it deducted from the monthly salary. It is crucial that provision is made for the payment of tax and Class 4 NI liabilities, and it is worth putting aside a reasonably substantial part of all income, a minimum of 30 per cent, on a monthly basis to build up sufficient funds to do so.

### Income records

An employee turns up for work, does his or her job, and gets paid at the end of the month. Pretty much the same happens with self-employment, except that there is a lot more paperwork involved, particularly keeping track of all the income, and making sure that all sums due are received.



- ▷ An invoice will need to be sent, on a monthly basis, to each practice for whom locum work is undertaken.
- ▷ Invoices must show the locum's name and address.
- ▷ Invoices need to identify the practice being invoiced and the basis of the fee, for example amounts due per session or per visit and the dates on which work was performed for the practice.
- ▷ Invoices should also be numbered sequentially.
- ▷ Each invoice should be marked, when payment is received, with the amount paid and the date of payment.
- ▷ Keep the invoices in a file in numbered order of issue, and totalled at the end of your accounting period.

### Expenditure records

Expenditure has to be faithfully recorded as well. This ensures that all expenditure is identified for the annual accounts, and that the maximum legitimate tax relief on the expenditure incurred is received. Broadly speaking, all expenditure that is incurred wholly and exclusively in the furtherance of a business is tax relievable. Naturally, in a system as complicated as the UK's tax regime there are myriad rules and exceptions, and vast volumes of case law dealing with this area, and this section can do no more than offer a brief overview of the more common areas. In this respect, seek advice from an accountant.

## MOTORING EXPENSES

There are two ways of dealing with motoring expenses, but either way will require a log to be kept of business miles. As a locum, the place of employment is the home, and mileage to and from clients' surgeries is considered to be business, as is of course mileage on home visits from the surgeries. This can be distinguished from the position in employment where getting to a place of work is always considered to be private mileage.

The easiest way of calculating your business motoring expense is to take the annual total for business miles, and multiply it by the HMRC-approved mileage rate. This rate is currently 40p per mile for the first 10,000 miles in a year, and then 25p for every mile thereafter. It is set at this level to take into account the capital depreciation of the vehicle.

The alternative way is to add up all the motoring expenses – tax, insurance, fuel, repairs, HP or loan interest – and apply a business percentage use. This percentage is calculated by taking the business miles as above, and dividing them by the total annual mileage (including private). So if the business use is 60 per cent, 60 per cent of your total motoring expenses are allowed against tax. In addition to this there is an entitlement to capital allowances on the capital cost of the car (25 per cent of the cost per annum subject to a maximum of £3000 for 2007/08, but reduced to 20 per cent of the cost per annum for 2008/09, still subject to a maximum of £3000), again multiplied by the business use.



## SUBSCRIPTIONS

Medical subscriptions are likely to be a major component of expenses. Fortunately, they are tax relievable, so annual costs incurred in respect of the General Medical Council (GMC), British Medical Association (BMA), Royal College of General Practitioners (RCGP), Medical Defence Union (MDU) and Medical Protection Society (MPS) for example would all be allowed in full.

## CONTINUING PROFESSIONAL DEVELOPMENT

Harsh as it might seem, significant elements of Continuing Professional Development will not attract tax relief. Only those elements of courses and training that update or reinforce existing knowledge will be allowable. Those costs incurred to increase expertise or leading to new qualifications, including exam fees, will not be allowed against tax.

OTHER EXPENSES

There will be other expenses that can be set against income, always going back to the 'wholly and exclusively incurred rule'. You would need to be able to show that these expenses would not have occurred had you not been employed in your particular line of work. This could include stationery and postage costs, and computer consumables, but not the capital cost of computers (which would be dealt with through the capital allowances computation where it would be likely to fall within the new 2008/09 100 per cent Annual Investment Allowance available on plant and machinery expenditure up to £50,000), accountancy fees and indeed any other costs that have been incurred in the furtherance of the business.

### ***Superannuation***



It is only comparatively recently that locum doctors have been able to be members of the highly regarded NHS pension scheme. As ever, there is a certain amount of form filling and administration necessary, and this needs to be borne in mind from the first days as a locum.

There are two main forms that need to be completed. The first is form *GP Locum A*, and this form has to be completed monthly for each practice where locum work is undertaken (one per practice per month). It details the amounts that have been earned as a locum from that practice in the month, and has to be attested by an authorised signatory (for example the practice manager). The second is form *GP Locum B*. This summarises the information on all the GP Locum A forms and is again completed monthly. It will therefore detail the total monthly locum income. A deduction of 10 per cent is made to allow for professional expenses, and then a variable percentage of the remaining 90 per cent is paid into the NHS scheme (The percentage paid is normally based on the amount earned in the previous year. Where the 2007/08 pay was up to £19,682, the rate payable for 2008/09 is 5 per cent, for 2007/08 pay between £19,683 and £65,002, the 2008/09 rate is 6.5 per cent, for 2007/08 pay between £65,003 and £102,499 the 2008/09 rate is 7.5 per cent, and where the 2007/08 pay was above £102,000, the 2008/09 rate is 8.5 per cent. These rates are not changed during the year, even if actual earnings would indicate a different contribution band). These forms must all be submitted monthly to the Primary Care Trust (PCT) and copies kept in case problems arise.

At the end of the year, the total superannuation paid (per tax year) is relieved through an entry on the tax return. It is not treated as a business expense in the accounts or as a deduction from total income.

### Annual accounts

Having kept the records assiduously through the year, they have to be collated in a form that will enable entries to be made on the tax return. The first thing that will have to be decided is the year end. The simplest date to select (and it is the taxpayer's choice) is the period to 31 March. It fits in nicely with the tax year end (actually 5 April but HMRC are prepared to treat the dates as the same) and is the easiest to understand as the income is more directly related to the tax paid for any one year. It also helps as the time spent as a locum might be brief if a partnership opportunity comes along at an early stage, and adjustments for commencement and cessation are minimised with a 31 March period end.

The income and expenditure account will be drawn up and the net profit for the period arrived at. This will have to be adjusted for tax purposes – disallowed expenses taken out, and capital allowances included – and it is this resultant figure that is assessable to tax.



### Accountants and administration

Of course the GP can prepare his or her own accounts, fill in his or her own tax returns, work out how to get tax relief on superannuation, deal with HMRC, work out how much tax to pay and when ... but the chances are it won't be correct. The more normal course of action is to employ an accountant, preferably a qualified specialist medical accountant, to do this on his or her behalf. It will cost a few hundred pounds a year (on most of which you will get tax relief) but the reward is peace of mind at not having anything to do with the 'tax authorities'.

There will inevitably be paperwork and formalities that have to be dealt with. *Form 64-8* will need to be signed. This is a form notifying HMRC that an agent has been appointed, and authorising HMRC to deal directly with the agent rather than the taxpayer. The taxpayer will still get copies of everything, but a buffer is interposed between them and HMRC.

The accountant will need to fulfil his or her professional obligation to identify the client, and will do this in most cases by asking for:

- confirmation of the GP's identity and address
- a copy of his or her passport
- a utility bill or bank statement addressed to the GP at his or her home address.

The accountant will also discuss the basis of his or her fees, and provide a letter of engagement. This is in essence the contract between the GP and the accountant setting out the respective responsibilities, and stating who is to do what and when. There will be two copies, each signed by both parties, one retained by the GP, the other by the accountant. Like partnership agreements, this is often never looked at, unless there is a problem!

## The GP as a partner

The next step in the career path for some locum GPs is to become a partner. Although a daunting step, from an accounting and tax point of view not a lot changes. The GP is still self-employed, and the tax rules on allowable expenditure are still the same, but instead of locum income being declared in the tax return, it is partnership income instead. Most of the above is still entirely relevant, with the main changes being in the complexities of partnership accounts and superannuation issues. There are extra responsibilities, notably those of running a much larger business with other people to be aware of, both partners and employees, but the rewards, both financial and in satisfaction terms, can also be greater.



### *Partnership agreement*

One of the first things to get to grips with is the partnership agreement when considering a partnership. For the purposes of the financial position it is worth making sure a few important questions are covered. Some GPs will use the BMA to ascertain statements in the partnership agreement (particularly if it hasn't been rewritten for a while), and some might consider discussing the financial aspects with an independent accountant, or discussing it in confidence with a more experienced GP (e.g. your trainer) if your new partnership is happy for the details to be shared. For example:

- what will be the profit share?
- how quickly is parity reached? (Some practices have a reduced share of the profits for new partners for 1–5 years, arguing that the new partner has a lower workload. This is a historical practice originating from when partners came on to take a new list and so genuinely had a lower workload. The practice is no longer universal, as personal lists no longer exist, and most GPs, whether new or established, work flat out)
- will money have to be introduced to finance working capital? Any practice will have a delay between work done and repayment by the PCTs, or medicines bought for the dispensary and reimbursement. This capital is shared by the partners in the business.

- ▷ once you know the capital it is important to know how quickly the money is made available. For instance in some cases the practice will allow an incoming partner to reduce his or her monthly drawings, and build up gradually, whilst some will require a lump sum after a specified time in practice
- ▷ is the surgery building owned by the practice? If so will you as an incoming partner need to raise finance (as a business loan like paying off a mortgage), and will your repayments be covered by your share of the rent paid to the practice by the PCT?
- ▷ how is the value of the surgery arrived at?
- ▷ what is the drawings policy of the practice? Do the partners take out as much as possible each month or do they assume a percentage reduction so that the practice doesn't get into financial difficulties, reclaiming that difference once the end-of-year accounts are known?
- ▷ is money retained in the practice to fund partners' tax liabilities?
- ▷ how quickly is any outgoing partner's capital account paid to him or her?



These are important questions, and often there is no one correct answer. The incoming partner will have to consider each point in turn, to determine his or her own attitude to the partnership's position. It is worth being wary of 'gentlemen's agreements', particularly when there is an issue of transfer of ownership of a building. Most agreements allow for a period of mutual assessment.

As part of appraising a potential partnership opportunity, sight of the previous year's accounts is essential. This will normally have comparative figures on, thus enabling the last two years to be examined. This will be considered in the next section, but it is likely that this will be the first time that full accounts will have been seen, so, again, discuss what they mean with an independent specialist medical accountant before becoming a partner.

### *Superannuation*

Superannuation has become more complex over the last few years. Whereas it always used to be calculated in a prescriptive manner by the NHS according to classes of work performed, it is now calculated by reference to the profits of the partnership and other private superannuable income. This has changed the emphasis from one of being advised by the NHS of the superannuable income to having to derive it and then advise the NHS.

The superannuation calculations, in broad terms, require profits both from the partnership and declared elsewhere on tax returns to be divided between those derived from NHS work and those from non-NHS work. Only that from

NHS work is superannuable. Because the superannuable income is now profit-based, the form cannot be prepared until after the partnership accounts, together with personal tax returns and expenses claims, have been finalised. This means that the forms for the year ended 31 March 2007 are unlikely to be prepared much before February 2008, with superannuation contributions being spread over two tax years – the payments on account in 2006/07 and the balancing amount (or refund) in March 2008.

A partner is required to contribute a variable percentage of the superannuable profits to the NHS pension scheme using the same bands and rates as stated in the section on locum superannuation above. This is treated as personal pension contributions and considered to be part of drawings. The practice is required to pay a further 14 per cent of superannuable earnings as employer's contributions. The problem here is that while practices will have received funding for the employer's contributions through their baseline or contract figure, this may not be enough to cover the full amount, or might in some cases exceed the full amount, in which case it must be repaid.



Payments are deducted during the year based on estimates provided by the practice, usually in conjunction with the practice accountant, with a balance figure due when year-end certificates of superannuable remuneration are prepared. The estimate can be altered at any time if the practice feels it is paying insufficiently, and it is in everyone's interest to get this estimate right to avoid sizeable liabilities in March, shortly after the tax bill has been paid in January.

### ***Personal expenses claim***

Not all the business expenses of the partner will be met by the partnership. What is, and what is not, will be covered in the partnership agreement, but it is usual that at least motor expenses and the capital cost of cars are kept outside the partnership accounts. This is principally due to the fact that the partners will have very different ideas as to what constitutes an appropriate car, and they will incur markedly different costs for servicing and fuel. Since personal attitudes, and pockets, differ, it is more appropriate to include such details on a personal expenses claim.

In fact, the personal expenses claim is much the same as the locum income and expenditure account, only without the income side. It will include all those expenses incurred in the furtherance of your business that are not included in the partnership accounts. It will usually include some medical subscriptions, and possibly professional indemnity insurance. It might also include an allowance for use of home as office, and accountancy fees for the preparation of the expenses claim.

The expenses claim, to obtain tax relief, has to be included on the partnership tax return, so it is important that this is prepared in a timely fashion to avoid delaying preparation of the partnership tax return. This in turn delays the other partners' tax returns. This then delays the calculation of tax liabilities. This consequently means that the partners won't know their liabilities at an early stage to allow them to make suitable provision for payment (or for the practice to know how big a cheque they will be required to write out).

## Partnership accounts

GP partnership accounts are like no other. Preparing them requires specialist knowledge, and it will take GPs a few years as a partner to fully get to grips with all the nuances contained within the separate schedules that together form the annual accounts.



### *Income schedule*

It is important that all the income streams are identified under separate headings. The main Personal Medical Services (PMS) or General Medical Services (GMS) income will be divided between the various categories:

- PMS or GMS contract income
- Directed Enhanced Services
- National Enhanced Services
- Local Enhanced Services
- quality payments
- seniority.

Dispensing income will be shown separately, as will other NHS income (PCT support, locums, meetings, premises costs: notional rent, cost rent, rent and rates reimbursements), followed by other superannuable income (PCT appointments, Professional Executive Committees [PEC] allowances) and finally other non-superannuable and private income (reports, examinations, cremation fees, occupational medicine, nursing homes). This list is by no means exhaustive as each practice will have its own particular income streams.

### *Expenditure schedule*

The expenditure, too, is divided into sections and will typically include:

- ▷ staff costs (salaries, pension contributions, training, recruitment)
- ▷ premises expenses (rent, rates, insurance, repairs and renewals, health centre costs)
- ▷ medical expenses (drugs, instruments, levy, consumables, locum fees, subscriptions)
- ▷ administration expenses (printing, postage, stationery, telephone, computer costs, sundries, legal and professional fees).

Both the income and expenditure schedules will include comparative figures for the previous year. This will highlight any significant variances and, if any are found, enable research to discover the reasons why.

### *Income and expenditure account (profit and loss account)*

This will just show the main headings and totals, and deduct the expenditure from the income to derive the net partnership profit for the year. This net profit figure will be divided between the partners in accordance with the profit-sharing ratio as set out in the partnership agreement. Account will be taken of any prior allocations of profit, for example through differing shares for seniority, employer's superannuation, premises income and costs, or private income. Again, it depends what is agreed between the partners in the partnership agreement.



### *Balance sheet*

The balance sheet looks at the position of the practice at a point in time – the year end. It itemises the assets of the partnership, splitting them between fixed assets (building, fixtures and fittings, computers) and current assets (stock, debtors – amounts owed to the practice – and prepayments, bank and cash accounts), and deducts the current liabilities (sums owed to third parties at the year end) to arrive at the net assets of the practice.

As the balance sheet 'balances', the net assets will exactly equal the total of the partners' funds (partners' capital accounts) retained in the business at the year end.

### *Partners' capital accounts*

This schedule will show all the movements on the partners' capital accounts through the year. It will commence with the balance brought forward at the start of the year, add in the share of profits for the year, and deduct all the amounts withdrawn. The withdrawals will include the monthly drawings and any bonuses, the employer's superannuation, any tax and National Insurance deducted at source on appointments, and any tax payments made through the practice. It will also include any *ad hoc* drawings to meet personal debts or in respect of those items that should properly be shown in personal expenses claims.

### *Notes to the accounts*

The notes to the accounts provide more details on items already shown on the main pages above. It includes movements on the fixed-asset accounts, depreciation, details of incentive scheme receipts and payments, accounting policies, and any other items where the accountants in conjunction with the partners feel further clarification is needed.



## Taxation

The UK's tax system is vast and complex, and getting more so by the year. This section can provide no more than the very briefest of overviews to put it into context. The main point to note is that everyone is assessed as an individual. This is so even if you are in partnership, so the points made below will apply to all, from the humblest locum to the senior partner in a big practice.

### *Tax return*

The starting point is the tax return. Assuming that the return is filed online, it must be submitted by 31 January following the tax year end on 5 April. The tax return pulls together all sources of income and details all personal allowances and reliefs. The number of entries on the return (which copes with all eventualities) is often fairly small, but it is the work behind making the entries that takes the time.

As far as self-employed or partnership accounts are concerned, taxation is based on the annual accounts ending in the tax year, so accounts for the year ended 31 March 2008 will be assessed for the tax year ended 5 April 2008 on the tax return, which must be submitted by 31 January 2009. Again, there is an automatic penalty of £100 for late submission (or tax due if less).

### *Tax payments*

The tax payable for any tax year is paid in three amounts. The first instalment (which is equal to one half of the previous year's liability) is due by 31 January in the tax year. The second instalment (also equal to one half of the previous year's liability) is due by 31 July following the tax year end, and the balancing amount (which may be a refund if the payments on account exceed the final liability) is due by 31 January following the tax year end. This is of course the same day that the tax return covering the same period is due, and also the first payment on account for the following year.

In circumstances where profits have risen materially, this system can lead to a significant rise in the amount of tax payable on 31 January. It is important that this is taken into account in cashflow planning, especially for example in the early years as a partner where income can increase sharply as the new partner moves to parity.

A simple example will illustrate the potential difficulties. Say that the tax liabilities are £20,000 for 2006/07, £20,000 for 2007/08, £29,000 for 2008/09, and £41,000 for 2009/10. The tax payable would be:



| | |
|---|---|
| January 2009 | £10,000 |
| July 2009 | £10,000 |
| January 2010 | £23,500 |
| July 2010 | £14,500 |
| January 2011 | £32,500 |
| July 2011 | £20,500 |

So, to look in more detail at the January 2011 payment, the payments on account for this year would have been January 2010, £14,500 (one half the 2008/09 liability) and July 2010, £14,500 (second instalment, one half the 2008/09 liability), giving a total payment on account of £29,000. There is therefore a balance due for 2009/10 of £12,000 (£41,000 minus £29,000). However, in addition to this, there is the first instalment for 2010/2011 due of £20,500 (one half of the 2009/10 liability). So the total payable for January 2011 is £32,500 (£12,000 plus £20,500). It can come as a rude awakening if this liability is not known well in advance, as well as putting a strain on relationships with other partners and the external accountant.

### *Tax calculation*

The mechanics of the tax calculation is in outline quite simple. It is the unusual items that serve to make it complicated. The starting point is the pulling together of all income. This will include interest, dividends, self-employed and partnership income, and anything else that should be assessed (cremation fees, lecture fees, authorship). Please note here that it is the taxpayer's responsibility to declare any untaxed income to the HMRC, not their job to discover it. That, and the resultant investigation fees, are best avoided.

The next stage is to deduct allowances and reliefs, for example personal tax allowances, superannuation payments and any professional loan interest (to buy the surgery building or to provide capital to the practice). The figure that is left is the taxable income, and it is then a case of working through the tax bands (taking into account higher-rate relief on pensions and gift aid payments) to arrive at the tax payable. In addition to this, there will be Class 4 NI payable on the business profits as detailed above. This is added in to the tax liability, payable in the same manner and at the same time as the tax is. These calculations are really best left to an accountant or the very brave, as the opportunities for error are legion. The HMRC online system is good, and does do the tax and NI calculations, but there is still the problem of working out exactly what information to put into which box.



## Managing the partnership finances

Being a partner is not just about being a doctor. The partner is also running a business, in conjunction with other co-owners, with a turnover often running into millions of pounds. The partners employ staff, manage buildings, and have to become businessmen, and this is before current schemes such as Practice-Based Commissioning and clinical budgets of several million are taken into account. As in all walks of life, there is a spread of natural ability within doctors and within practices in this area! Particular attention needs to be paid to the *cashflow* of the business, as there will be some significant outgoings at particular times of the year, and, with the possible exception of QoF payments, income is likely to be more uniform month by month. All this needs to be factored in. Not only do the staff need paying, but also the partners need to have a strategy for withdrawing funds for themselves that does not adversely impact the partnership cashflow.

### *Drawings*

This is probably the key area, from which all good financial management stems. There are two contrasting alternatives to a drawings policy.

The first is to work out how much money is in the bank at the end of the month, allow for cheques to be paid, both written but 'unpresented' and those amounts that need paying at the month end, and then split the remaining balance between the partners in accordance with the profit-sharing ratio, drawing the whole lot out. There are a number of problems with this approach:

- there is little scope to cope with unforeseen, perhaps major, expenditure
- the drawings for each partner varies from month to month according to the funds in the bank
- each partner will be left to fund their own tax liabilities. As illustrated above, the last of these could present real problems if individual financial management is lacking.

A lot will depend on the practice manager's understanding of the practice finances, as it is often him or her who performs the monthly calculations.

The second approach will involve the external accountant. It is more complex (therefore more expensive) but will assist enormously in the smooth running of the practice. Here, an estimate will be made of the likely annual profits of the practice, and the tax and superannuation liabilities will be calculated and deducted from each partner's share of the profits, with the balance being the expected available drawings for the year. A deduction of 10 per cent (say) can be made to allow for a drop in profits or to provide additional working capital, with the remaining balance being divided by 12 to give an equalised monthly drawing figure. This is drawn every month. As there were disadvantages to the first approach, there are only advantages to this approach – on the assumption that the profits were forecast reasonably accurately in the first place:

- full allowance has been made for the tax liability, and, since this has not been drawn, a fund is built up in the practice to meet the liabilities as they fall due
- the partners are able to spend all they draw should they so wish, without having to think about what the tax liabilities are or when they are due
- if the profits are as expected, there is the 10 per cent undrawn that can either be distributed as a bonus to the partners, or retained in the practice to finance future expansion through increased working capital or a combination of them both.

While on the subject of drawings, there is a common misconception that tax is charged on the amounts taken from the practice as drawings. This is emphatically not the case. Taxation is charged on the partner's share of the profits of the practice, as shown in the accounts, adjusted for tax purposes, however much is drawn. Drawings are merely sums taken out on account of the profits. They may be more than, or less than, the share of profits. Whichever it is, the tax liability is unaltered.

### *Superannuation*

Just as there needs to be awareness for cashflow purposes as to when the tax liabilities are due, there is also a need to be aware that there is a balancing payment for superannuation due in March. This is unfortunately going to be difficult to quantify much in advance, as it requires both the annual practice accounts and individual tax returns to be prepared beforehand. Since tax returns (despite best intentions) are often not prepared until January, there is little time to prepare figures in advance. It only needs one partner to delay providing his or her personal information to the accountant to delay the preparation of the partnership tax return, which in turn delays the superannuation forms. However, it should be possible to provide a reasoned estimate by looking at the shortfall of the previous year, and working out whether profits have increased or not, to estimate a final total liability, and then comparing this with the superannuation payments on account made throughout the year.



### *Tax liabilities*

Having suggested that drawings are restricted to allow for the tax liabilities, the practice manager and partners must always take into account what the liabilities are and when they are due, as there can often be substantial sums in the practice bank accounts retained to meet the liabilities. The temptation to spend this money must be avoided. One way to deal with this is to make a monthly transfer into a separate high-interest 'tax account' such that, when the tax is due, sufficient separate funds will have accumulated in this account to make the payment without raiding the day-to-day working capital in the current account.

---

## Conclusion

It can be seen that there is a vast amount of information to take in when starting and running a self-employed business, and GPs are no different from anyone else in this respect. The learning curve is steep indeed, encompassing dealing with HMRC, record-keeping, accounting to the NHS for superannuation payments and preparing tax returns. Further on, perhaps even more complex issues have to be faced with partnership agreements, expenses claims, annual accounts, different superannuation rules and their interaction with partnership and personal tax returns.

This chapter can only give a flavour of the issues and considerations on what is a huge subject, but it will, hopefully, aid those starting out in business by giving them at least some idea of the questions that should be asked.

## Questions

**1** ▷ What is the time limit for notifying HMRC that self-employment has commenced?

**2** ▷ What is a form 64–8?

**3** ▷ What two classes of National Insurance do the self-employed pay?

**4** ▷ What rates of superannuation are paid as a GP locum?

**5** ▷ What date does the tax year end on?

**6** ▷ What date is the deadline for filing tax returns online?

**7** ▷ What is the main difference between a locum GP income and expenditure account, and a partner's expenses claim?

**8** ▷ Are tax liabilities based on profit share or drawings?

**9** ▷ What effect does a rapidly rising share of profits have on the pattern of tax payments?

**10** ▷ What are the advantages of an equalised monthly drawings system?

## Appendix 1

### *Dr F – locum income and expenditure account for the year ended 31 March 2007*

| | £ | £ | £ |
|---|---|---|---|
| **Income** | | | 42,500 |
| **Expenditure** | | | |
| Motor vehicle | | | |
| Petrol | 2450 | | |
| Insurance | 450 | | |
| Tax | 150 | | |
| Repairs and maintenance | 750 | | |
| Hire purchase interest | 1100 | | |
| | 4900 | | |
| Less: private use 40% | 1960 | | |
| | | 2940 | |
| Professional subscriptions | | | |
| MPS | | 3400 | |
| BMA | | 250 | |
| GMC | | 290 | |
| Family planning | | 70 | |
| Telephone, business use | | 75 | |
| Postage and stationery | | 45 | |
| Use of home as office | | 260 | |
| Accountancy | | 600 | |
| | | | 7930 |
| **Net profit for the period** | | | 34,570 |

I approve this income and expenditure account and confirm that I have made available all relevant records and information for its preparation.

Dated the .......................................... day of .......................................... 2007

Signed ..........................................................................................................

### Accountant's report

In accordance with instructions given to us, we have prepared, without carrying out an audit, the income and expenditure account from the accounting records of Dr F and from information and explanations supplied to us.

Smith & Jones
Chartered Accountants
1 Anywhere Road
Generictown
Anyshire AB1 2CD

---

## Appendix 2

**ABCDE HEALTH CENTRE PRACTICE – FINANCIAL STATEMENTS FOR THE YEAR ENDED 31 MARCH 2007**



### Contents

| | |
|---|---|
| Accountant's report | *Page 1* |
| Income and expenditure account | *2 and 3* |
| Analysis of expenditure | *4* |
| Balance sheet | *5* |
| Partners' capital account | *6* |
| Notes to the accounts | *7 and 8* |

---

*Page 1*

In accordance with the engagement letter dated 31 March 2007, we approve the financial information which comprises the Financial Statements on the following pages x to y. We acknowledge our responsibility for the financial information, and for providing Smith & Jones with all information and explanations necessary for its compilation.

***Signed***

Dr A ..........................................................................................

Dr B ..........................................................................................

Dr C ..........................................................................................

Dr D ..........................................................................................

Dr E ..........................................................................................

Dated the .......................................... day of .......................................... 2007

## *Chartered accountants' report to ABCDE Health Centre Practice on the unaudited financial statements*

In accordance with the engagement letter dated 31 March 2007, we have compiled the financial information of ABCDE Health Centre Practice which comprises the Income and Expenditure Account, Balance Sheet and related schedules from the accounting records and information and explanations you have given to us.

The financial information is not intended to achieve full compliance with the provisions of UK Generally Accepted Accounting Principles.

This report is made to you, in accordance with the terms of our engagement. Our work has been undertaken so that we might compile the financial information that we have been engaged to compile, report to you that we have done so, and state those matters that we have agreed to state to you in this report and for no other purpose. To the fullest extent permitted by law, we do not accept or assume responsibility to anyone other than ABCDE Health Centre Practice for our work or for this report.

We have carried out this engagement in accordance with technical guidance issued by the Institute of Chartered Accountants in England and Wales, and have complied with the ethical guidance laid down by the Institute.

You have approved the financial information for the year ended 31 March 2007 and have acknowledged your responsibility for it, for the appropriateness of the accounting basis and for providing all information and explanations necessary for its compilation.

We have not verified the accuracy or completeness of the accounting records or information and explanations you have given to us and we do not, therefore, express any opinion on the financial information.

Smith & Jones
Chartered Accountants
1 Anywhere Road
Generictown
Anyshire AB1 2CD

Page 2

***ABCDE Health Centre Practice income and expenditure account for the year ended 31 March 2007***

| | | **2007** | | 2006 |
|---|---|---|---|---|
| | **£** | **£** | £ | £ |
| **PMS income** | | | | |
| PMS contract | | **57,5000** | | 54,0000 |
| **Directed Enhanced Services** | | | | |
| Enhanced access | **15,000** | | 9000 | |
| Influenza immunisations | **11,400** | | 12,500 | |
| Pneumovax | **1650** | | 1700 | |
| Practice-Based Commissioning | **14,500** | | – | |
| Choose and Book | **6100** | | – | |
| Information management and technology | **2800** | | – | |
| | | **51,450** | | 23,200 |
| **National Enhanced Services** | | | | |
| Substance misuse | **2750** | | 4000 | |
| Obesity | **–** | | 850 | |
| Methotrexate monitoring | **1400** | | 1000 | |
| Anti-coagulation | **7000** | | 5000 | |
| | | **11,150** | | 10,850 |
| **Local Enhanced Services** | | | | |
| Hormone implants | **400** | | 300 | |
| DVT | **1600** | | 900 | |
| Retinal photography | **6150** | | 6000 | |
| Smoking cessation | **300** | | 700 | |
| GP unit and Care in the Community | **7400** | | 9000 | |
| Minor surgery | **1200** | | 1100 | |
| Menorrhagia management | **100** | | 450 | |
| Primary prevention CHD | **2100** | | 1400 | |
| Phlebotomy | **2500** | | 2200 | |

| | | *2007* | | *2006* |
|---|---|---|---|---|
| | **£** | **£** | £ | £ |
| Care homes | **2400** | | 2100 | |
| Cervical screening | **500** | | 600 | |
| Insulin | **1100** | | – | |
| | | **25,750** | | 24,750 |
| **Quality payments** | | | | |
| Aspiration | **85,000** | | 76,500 | |
| Achievement | **52,000** | | 62,000 | |
| | | **137,000** | | 138,500 |

*Page 3*



| | | | | |
|---|---|---|---|---|
| **PCO administered** | | | | |
| Seniority | | **20,300** | | 21,000 |
| **Dispensing income** | | **38,000** | | 36,000 |
| **Other NHS income** | | | | |
| PCT support and locums | **4200** | | 13,600 | |
| Pharmacist meetings | **1950** | | 1800 | |
| QoF visit | **1750** | | 1300 | |
| | | **7900** | | 16,700 |
| **Total NHS income** | | **866,550** | | 811,000 |
| **Other superannuable income** | | | | |
| PCT appointment | – | | 3500 | |
| PEC allowance | **4000** | | 9500 | |
| | | **4000** | | 13,000 |
| **Other non-superannuable income** | | | | |
| Insurance examinations etc. | **20,000** | | 20,000 | |
| Cremations | **3500** | | 3000 | |
| Speaker fees | **1600** | | 850 | |
| | | **25,100** | | 23,850 |
| **Interest received** | | **2500** | | 1150 |

| | | 2007 | | 2006 |
|---|---|---|---|---|
| | £ | £ | £ | £ |
| **Incentive scheme receipts** | | **16,800** | | 14,500 |
| **Total income** | | **914,950** | | 863,500 |
| **Expenditure per attached schedule** | | **467,050** | | 426,000 |
| **Net income for the period** | | **447,900** | | 437,500 |

*Page 4*

| | | | | |
|---|---|---|---|---|
| **Employment and subcontract costs** | | | | |
| Practice staff salaries | **230,000** | | 210,000 | |
| Assistant's salary | **35,000** | | 24,500 | |
| Pensions contributions | **32,000** | | 30,000 | |
| Training expenses | **2150** | | 650 | |
| Recruitment costs | **1600** | | 450 | |
| Staff welfare | **1200** | | 1800 | |
| Uniforms | **650** | | – | |
| | | **302,600** | | 267,400 |
| **Premises expenses** | | | | |
| Rent | **22,300** | | 21,500 | |
| Insurance | **850** | | 800 | |
| Repairs and renewals | **4500** | | 2100 | |
| Health centre charges | **32,650** | | 28,500 | |
| | | **60,300** | | 52,900 |
| **Medical administration expenses** | | | | |
| Drugs | **29,000** | | 27,000 | |
| Consumables | **3200** | | 2600 | |
| NHS levies | **1800** | | 1600 | |
| Locum fees | **12,600** | | 22,800 | |
| Medical imaging | **2000** | | 2150 | |
| Professional indemnity insurance | **16,000** | | 15,000 | |
| Medical subscriptions | **1800** | | 1750 | |
| | | **66,400** | | 72,900 |

| | | ***2007*** | | *2006* |
|---|---|---|---|---|
| | **£** | **£** | £ | £ |
| **Administration expenses** | | | | |
| Printing, postage and stationery | **2600** | | 2400 | |
| Telephone | **3200** | | 2750 | |
| Travelling expenses | **100** | | 150 | |
| Advertising | **250** | | 100 | |
| Computer costs | **2650** | | 850 | |
| Sundries | **2000** | | 2650 | |
| | | **10,800** | | 8900 |
| **Professional fees** | | | | |
| Accountancy fees | **8400** | | 7500 | |
| Legal fees | **800** | | 850 | |
| | | **9200** | | 8350 |
| **Financial expenses** | | | | |
| Bank charges and interest | | **300** | | 250 |
| **Depreciation** | | **650** | | 800 |
| **Incentive scheme payments** | | **16,800** | | 14,500 |
| **Total expenditure** | | **467,050** | | 426,000 |

*Page 5*

| | £ | **2007** £ | £ | 2006 £ |
|---|---|---|---|---|
| **Partners' accounts (per schedule)** | | | | |
| Dr A | | **13,125** | | 15,000 |
| Dr B | | **12,175** | | 14,500 |
| Dr C | | **10,433** | | 10,500 |
| Dr D | | **8983** | | 7500 |
| Dr E | | **8384** | | 7500 |
| | | **53,100** | | 55,000 |
| Computer equipment | | **600** | | 800 |
| Fixtures and fittings | | **2550** | | 3000 |
| | | **3150** | | 3800 |
| **Current assets** | | | | |
| Stock of drugs | **2800** | | 2300 | |
| Cash at bank | **36,000** | | 47,250 | |
| Cash in hand | **50** | | 50 | |
| Debtors and prepayments | **102,500** | | 96,000 | |
| | **141,350** | | 145,600 | |
| **Current liabilities** | | | | |
| Creditors and accruals | **77,100** | | 78,000 | |
| Superannuation reserve account | **14,300** | | 16,400 | |
| | **91,400** | | 94,400 | |
| **Net current assets (liabilities)** | | **49,950** | | 51,200 |
| | | **53,100** | | 55,000 |

*Page 6*

| | Total | Dr A | Dr B | Dr C | Dr D | Dr E |
|---|---|---|---|---|---|---|
| | **£** | **£** | **£** | **£** | **£** | **£** |
| **Current account** | | | | | | |
| Balance at 1 April 2006 | **55,000** | 15,000 | 14,500 | 10,500 | 7500 | 7500 |
| Profit share | **447,900** | 111,975 | 111,975 | 78,383 | 78,383 | 67,184 |
| | **502,900** | 126,975 | 126,475 | 88,883 | 85,883 | 74,684 |
| Monthly drawings | **369,500** | 93,500 | 94,000 | 64,000 | 63,500 | 54,500 |
| Other payments | **1150** | 200 | 250 | 650 | – | 50 |
| **Superannuation reserve** | | | | | | |
| Paid re. 2006/2007 | **64,850** | 16,250 | 16,250 | 11,300 | 11,300 | 9750 |
| Balance re. 2006/2007 | **14,300** | 3900 | 3800 | 2500 | 2100 | 2000 |
| | **449,800** | 113,850 | 114,300 | 78,450 | 76,900 | 66,300 |
| Balance at 31 March 2007 | **53,100** | 13,125 | 12,175 | 10,433 | 8983 | 8384 |

*Page 7*

**1 Profit shares**

| | Profit share Ratio % | Profit share ***2007*** | *2006* |
|---|---|---|---|
| | | **£** | £ |
| Dr A | **25.0** | **111,975** | 109,375 |
| Dr B | **25.0** | **111,975** | 109,375 |
| Dr C | **17.5** | **78,383** | 76,563 |
| Dr D | **17.5** | **78,383** | 76,563 |
| Dr E | **15.0** | **67,184** | 65,624 |
| | **100.0** | **447,900** | 437,500 |

## 2 Accounting policies

a) Income and expenditure

The income and expenditure account is prepared on an accruals basis so as to reflect actual income earned and expenditure incurred during the year

b) Stock of drugs

The stock of drugs is valued at the lower of cost or net realisable value

c) Fixed assets and depreciation

Fixed assets are written off over their estimated useful lives. The following rates of depreciation are applied to the assets in use at the balance sheet date:

| | |
|---|---|
| Computer equipment | 25% per annum reducing balance |
| Fixtures and fittings | 15% per annum reducing balance |



## 3 Fixed assets

| | Computer equipment | Fixtures and fittings | Total |
|---|---|---|---|
| | £ | £ | £ |
| **Cost** | | | |
| At 1 April 2006 | 6000 | 20,000 | 26,000 |
| Additions | — | 1500 | 1500 |
| Grants received | — | - 1500 | - 1500 |
| At 31 March 2007 | 6000 | 20,000 | 26,000 |
| **Depreciation** | | | |
| At 1 April 2006 | 5200 | 17,000 | 22,200 |
| Charge for the period | 200 | 450 | 650 |
| At 31 March 2007 | 5400 | 17,450 | 22,850 |
| **Net book value** | | | |
| At 31 March 2007 | 600 | 2550 | 3150 |
| At 31 March 2006 | 800 | 3000 | 3800 |

Page 8

**4 Seniority awards**

| | **2007** | *2006* |
|---|---|---|
| | **£** | £ |
| Dr A | **8500** | 8200 |
| Dr B | **6200** | 5900 |
| Dr C | **2800** | 4400 |
| Dr D | **1900** | 1800 |
| Dr E | **900** | 700 |
| | **20,300** | 21,000 |



**5 Incentive scheme**

| | **2007** | *2006* |
|---|---|---|
| | **£** | £ |
| Revenue savings received | **16,800** | 14,500 |
| Capital savings received | **1500** | 8000 |
| | **18,300** | 22,500 |
| **Capital expenditure** | | |
| Equipment and furniture | **1500** | 8000 |
| **Revenue expenditure** | | |
| Training | **7900** | 6000 |
| Locum fees | **2250** | 800 |
| Computer costs | **1500** | 2150 |
| Sundry medical expenditure | **1250** | 1000 |
| Repairs and renewals | **3250** | 4400 |
| Subscriptions | **200** | – |
| Printing | **450** | 150 |
| | **16,800** | 14,500 |

# The GP practice as an employer

# 7

*Jim Waits*

### *Scenario*

*You have been asked by the partners to assume the lead responsibility for staff and premises with the practice manager. After a meeting with the manager you decide that jointly you need to start by:*

- ▷ *undertaking an audit of the practice's compliance with legislative requirements related to staff employment and providing a safe working environment*
- ▷ *reviewing the effective use of staff in a challenging financial climate.*



### Introduction

This chapter aims to bridge the chapters on accounting and those on motivating a team and the primary healthcare team. Employment law and practice is becoming increasingly sophisticated so this chapter does not claim to provide all the answers, but hopes to introduce a newly qualified GP to some of the issues faced in employing individuals, and is written from experience in running a practice.

### The GP as a principal/business partner

In Chapter 6 Richard Lambert described how GP principals set themselves up as a legal partnership. It should be clear already that GP practices are small- to medium-size businesses and need to be managed in a business-like manner.

Partners, as owners of the business, are not paid salaries but rely on a profitable business for their income: the higher the income and/or the lower the expenses the greater the profit.

Practice income is very crudely generated by the number of patients on the list as well as the level of services offered (see Chapter 1 for the Quality and Outcomes Framework [QoF]). The appendices to Chapter 6 show that other activity, training GP registrars, medical students, offering occupational health services also brings in income, albeit often on a much smaller scale. Increasingly practices see themselves as being in competition with other practices for patients, and being sensitive to patients' expectations will be an essential aspect of practice business management in the coming years.

Staff costs, including locums and any practice contribution to the Out-of-Hours service, will amount to 75–80 per cent of the total practice spend. The balance will be made up of drugs and instruments (about 8 per cent), premises expenses (5 per cent), medical defence subscriptions (3 per cent). Effective control of staff costs should be a high priority in any practice, though this is not to dismiss the importance of closely monitoring other items of spend.

In many practices individual partners will take a lead responsibility for different aspects of running the business, including:



- ▷ finance
- ▷ patients' services
- ▷ premises
- ▷ staff matters

whilst other partners will lead on registrar training etc.

Most modern practices will have a practice manager with some business qualification or experience. The term 'lead responsibility' used above is not to suggest that the partner will produce the payroll or change the light bulbs, but to describe how one partner will liaise with the practice manager on these issues and reflect the partners' likely point of view on any problem that needs to be resolved.

The authority and responsibility delegated to the practice manager, or to an individual partner, will vary significantly from practice to practice. In some practices, spending relatively small sums requires the unanimous agreement of all partners; in others the practice manager will have authority to manage expenditure within an annual budget.

---

## Employment of staff

Employment law is highly regulated, complex and tends to favour the employee. The influence of European attitudes to employment law is growing; for example, the statutory minimum holiday entitlement increases by four days (to 24 days) in October 2007 and an additional four days in October 2008. Whilst these minimal requirements include bank holidays, most practices might feel morally bound to add these days of leave to existing provisions.

It is important to understand that, whilst the GP practice is of the NHS, it is not, generally, required to adhere to NHS terms and conditions of service for staff. One exception, for example, is the requirement that salaried doctors in General Medical Services (GMS) practices (but not in Personal Medical Services [PMS] practices) must be employed on the model contract agreed nationally. The exceptions are few.

The practice is, however, required to comply with legislation related to staff employment too numerous to cite here. This includes the requirements:

- to issue a contract of employment within two months of the commencement date – legally the requirement is not to issue a contract within this time-frame but rather a statement of obligations; however, practices should not rely on this technicality
- not to discriminate on the grounds of age, disability, race, religion, sex, etc. The employer must also not discriminate against part-time workers. Discrimination can be direct, e.g. refusal to appoint someone because of his or her sex, or indirect, e.g. when the employer advertises a post with a criterion that effectively prevents a group of people applying for the post
- not to dismiss the employee unfairly
- to grant Statutory Maternity Leave for a minimum of 26 weeks during which time she is entitled to benefit from all her normal terms and conditions of employment other than remuneration. She is, however, entitled to be paid Statutory Maternity Pay of 90 per cent of her average remuneration for the first six weeks and then for the next 20 weeks a weekly amount determined by the government each year. The practice can recover most of this payment from the government. A woman is entitled to take up to 26 additional weeks of maternity leave, i.e. up to 52 weeks in total
- to Statutory Sick Pay, Redundancy Pay, etc.

You will appreciate that the impact of legislative requirements can be onerous on a practice, sometimes making it difficult to maintain services to patients.

Most practices consult a solicitor if any advice on legislative requirements is needed. There is little provision for practices having access to NHS personnel or human resources departments for advice, though this might be available in some parts of the country. An excellent source of advice is the Advisory, Conciliation and Arbitration Service (ACAS), at www.acas.org.uk.

Keeping abreast of legislative changes can be time-consuming. Failing to comply with new legislation, or missing a significant change, is potentially damaging and most practice managers subscribe to advice services offered by 'Croner' in their publication *Practice and Primary Care Management* (which also provides regular updates; see www.croner.co.uk) or a similar organisation to safeguard the interest of the practice.

The QoF funding through the 'GMS2' contract (see Chapter 1) includes sections related to the employment of staff. The practice is not obliged to adhere to the requirements of the QoF but will gain points awarded for the following:

- ▷ all new staff receive induction training – *Education 4*
- ▷ there is a record of all practice-employed staff having attended training/ updating in basic life support skills in the preceding 36 months – *Education 5*
- ▷ all practice-employed nurses have Personal Learning Plans that have been reviewed at annual appraisal – *Education 8*
- ▷ all practice-employed non-clinical team members have an annual appraisal – *Education 9*
- ▷ producing a job description and person specification for the last vacancy advertised in the financial year – *Management 6*
- ▷ there is a written procedures manual that includes staff employment policies including equal opportunities, bullying and harassment, and sickness absence (including illegal drugs, alcohol and stress), to which staff have access – *Management 10.*



Practices are also able to earn funds from Direct Enhanced Services (DES, decided nationally; see Chapter 1) and Local Enhanced Services (LES, decided by the Primary Care Trust [PCT] in consultation with the Local Medical Committee [LMC]), some of which have implications for staff management. For example, the Information and Management Technology DES includes the requirement that staff must have their IT training needs identified and an individual training log must be completed for each member of staff. A practice training log must also be prepared. The DES and LES are not mandatory.

---

## Contracts of employment

NHS terms and conditions of service for staff are not used in most practices when writing contracts of employment, though a small number of practices have adopted some elements of Agenda for Change (a national NHS-wide review of the responsibilities of clinical employees' roles and the payment that should be offered for each). In order to attract clinical staff from secondary care and from PCT salaried posts many practices are looking at the

'Agenda for Change' bands on which to base pay scales or salaries.

Rates of pay are decided by the partners and need not be common to all staff in a particular group. For example, long-serving nursing staff are likely to be paid the former Whitley Council salaries (grades D, E, F or G). These were incremental scales intended to recognise that staff gained experience over time; the scales were increased each year by a nationally agreed inflation figure. Staff appointed more recently might have been offered a salary that is not on an incremental scale and not related to any recognised NHS salary.

The government decided not to increase practice income to pay for a staff inflation award in 2005/06, 2006/07 or 2007/08, and did not give any indication of an amount that it thought appropriate for practice staff. As a consequence it was left to partners in individual practices to decide the inflation award for staff in these two years. Whilst some practices continued to give annual increases to match inflation or to match the basic increase in line with other NHS-employed staff, some practices decided not to award staff any increase for inflation. Where inflation awards were agreed many practice managers were required to identify savings (in staff or other costs) to contribute to the cost of the increase. It is worth repeating at this point that the partners are running a small- to medium-size business and any increase in costs not funded by an increase in income means a reduction in profit and hence a reduction in partners' income.

Contracts of employment will usually include the following headings:

- title of post
- date employment started
- continuity of employment. Normally previous employment in the NHS is not counted if an employee transfers to a practice, which has an impact on the period counted towards maternity leave entitlement etc.
- rate of pay
- hours of work – most staff work part-time and might be required to accept in the contract that they will work flexibly to meet the particular requirements of general practice
- annual leave entitlement – it is usual for staff to be awarded extra days of leave after five or more years of service. Staff turnover can be very disruptive in a small business and rewards for continuity of service might help to encourage staff to stay
- maternity pay entitlement – it is usual for the entitlement to be limited to the statutory requirement even for salaried doctors in PMS practices. In GMS practices a salaried doctor will have the model contract, which is more generous than this
- pension scheme – staff in GP practices are entitled to join, or remain

members of, the NHS pension scheme and the practice pays the employer's contribution of 14 per cent of superannuable pay

- notice of termination of employment – an employee is entitled to one week's notice for each year of service up to 12 years
- grievance procedure
- disciplinary procedure
- health and safety at work procedures
- sickness policy and guidelines – the payment for staff on extended sick leave is likely to be much less generous than that applied to staff working in the NHS. A maximum entitlement of eight weeks of full pay and four weeks of half pay is not unusual in practices.

The contract will also refer to other staff policies, e.g. harassment and bullying at work policy, common to all staff and kept on a separate file accessible to everyone.



## Compliance with legislation and regulations

In this chapter I can refer only to some examples of the varied and onerous non-employment legislation imposed on businesses. This includes:

- numerous acts related to health and safety at work, principally the Health and Safety at Work etc. Act 1974. The act requires organisations to display a health and safety law poster setting out the legal requirements of the act, and also to display a copy of the current certificate for the Employers' Liability Compulsory Insurance. A practice must decide how it is going to manage health and safety in the business, and if it has five or more employees then this must be written down. The complexity and longstanding nature of the legislation can lead to a degree of complacency, but practices would be wise to review their risks regularly. A useful source of advice is the Health and Safety Executive website at www.hse.gov.uk. NHS organisations have been prosecuted and fined for failings
- the employer is required under the Health and Safety at Work Act to provide
    - a safe place of work
    - a safe means of access to work
    - a safe system of working
    - adequate equipment and material

and employ competent fellow employees and protect the employee from unnecessary risk of injury

- health and safety legislation also imposes obligations on employees. They must take reasonable care for their own health and safety, and that of others. The must co-operate with the employer to comply with any relevant legal obligations
- fire – the Regulatory Reform (Fire Safety) Order 2005 imposed new requirements in October 2006. Responsibility for complying with the Fire Safety Order rests with the *'responsible person'*. In practice this is the employer, i.e. the partners, although the practice manager is often the named person who will ensure that they must take all reasonable steps to work with each other. The responsible person must:
  - carry out a fire risk assessment, which must focus on safety in case of fire
  - pay particular attention to those at special risk, such as the disabled and those with special needs
  - have consideration of any dangerous substance likely to be on the premises, e.g. liquid nitrogen

  The fire risk assessment helps to identify risks that can be removed or reduced, and to decide the nature and extent of the general fire precautions needed to protect people against the fire risks that remain. A practice that employs five or more people must record the significant findings of the assessment. Every practice should ensure that regular fire drills are performed, fire extinguishers are checked annually, etc. A more detailed review can be found on www.communities.gov.uk/fire/firesafety
- the Data Protection Act 1998, which incorporates the requirements of the previous Access to Health Records Act, imposes strict conditions on how data collected by the practice can be used. It allows patients to request copies of data held by the practice on payment of a small fee. The Information Commissioner's Office is responsible for the protection of personal information (see www.ico.gov.uk) and provides a number of useful good-practice guides, e.g. *The Use of Violent Warning Markers* and *Subject Access to Health Records*. It is worth noting that requests for access to records relating to the deceased will continue to be made under the Access to Health Records Act 1990
- Disability Discrimination Act 2005 (DDA) amended and extended rights included in the corresponding act of 1995. It does not require that every part of a practice must be accessible to the public. However, a practice is expected to take all reasonable steps to provide access to the

disabled, incurring modest expenditure if necessary. This could include, for example, the provision of a mobile loop to help those with hearing difficulties. Information about the DDA implications for employment can be found on the Department for Work and Pensions website (www.dwp.gov.uk) and for more general advice the Disability Rights Commission website (www.drc.org.uk) is useful.

---

## Performance management

In this section I will refer to:

- ▷ effective use of resources
- ▷ monitoring the performance of staff.



### *Effective use of resources*

It is incumbent on the practice manager with business experience to review the use of resources regularly. However, every partner and member of staff has a role to play in suggesting more effective ways of working. Staff could be encouraged by a reward scheme, perhaps proportionate to the savings achievable. In this section I will refer to and give examples of:

- ▷ effective use of staff time
- ▷ premises and other non-staff costs
- ▷ new initiatives.

#### EFFECTIVE USE OF STAFF TIME

An example here is where a practice manager could review with the senior practice nurse whether duties undertaken by qualified nurses could be fulfilled by a healthcare assistant. Qualified nurse time freed could then be used to introduce new services to patients, e.g. nurse-led clinics in a designated specialty. To extend the use of resources as effectively as possible, such clinics could in turn free medical staff time for more patients' appointments. However, such a review could also lead to a reduction in qualified nursing time or medical staff time and thus generate a financial saving to the practice, or free up funds for employing other staff elsewhere.

#### *LOOKING AT INFORMATION SYSTEM MANAGEMENT*

For example, a practice manager could identify the time previously spent filing pathology results that are now transmitted electronically to the practice and automatically attached to patients' records. Unless an administrative task has been identified as needing more staff time the expectation should be a reduction in these hours and a consequential financial saving to the practice.

Most practices now scan all incoming documents, and doctors and nurses use the computer to record consultations etc. Considerable administrative staff time might be saved by this initiative. Similar technological initiatives should see further reductions in administrative staff time.

#### PREMISES AND OTHER NON-STAFF COSTS

Competition between utility companies should be used by the practice manager to pursue financial savings. This is an initiative easily missed as the companies increase charges by stealth.

Vaccine costs are negotiable and the practice manager or senior practice nurse should ensure that the prices of flu vaccines, for example, are reviewed every year.

#### NEW INITIATIVES

IT should enable a practice to reduce the time spent by administrative staff on routine tasks. For example, giving patients the opportunity to book and cancel appointments by the internet will reduce administrative time considerably, and financial savings should be achieved.

### *Monitoring the performance of staff*

The nature of the general practice surgery is such that most staff develop a loyalty to their colleagues that is seen less often in large organisations. In this section I will outline management's role in:

1. setting and reviewing performance standards
2. counselling under-performing staff
3. managing sickness absence
4. dismissal of staff.

## SETTING AND REVIEWING PERFORMANCE STANDARDS

Management of staff can be summarised as:

1 ▷ plan what needs to be done

2 ▷ delegate the task to staff of an appropriate grade, ensuring they have been trained to do the work

3 ▷ monitor that the work is done and within the timescale necessary

4 ▷ revise the plan if necessary and revert to point 1.

Some tasks would reveal themselves as 'done', or 'not done', very quickly, e.g. the preparation of the payroll. Other tasks are not so easily monitored. There is always a given that most staff will behave with integrity (why would you employ someone you didn't trust?) and undertake the tasks given to them promptly, but good management should ensure that this is always case.



In the smaller business malingering and time-wasting is generally less prevalent than in the large organisation, often because it is harder for the employee to hide. Peer pressure can be very successful in stopping abuse of the goodwill shown to staff. Nevertheless, the practice manager, in particular, needs to ensure that procedures are in place to set appropriate standards for the staff, to monitor the standards set and take remedial action if necessary. For example, most practices will have a modern telephone system that will allow the practice manager to review the time it has taken for incoming calls to be answered, and, if this causes concern, to establish whether the staff who should be responding to the calls are doing so in a timely manner.

### *THE USE OF PROTOCOLS IN SETTING STANDARDS*

A challenge in a small- to medium-size business is how to identify those protocols that are essential and require that staff adhere to them. Too many protocols can create an atmosphere of bureaucracy, discouraging staff from putting forward initiatives and stifling professional enthusiasm. However, a lack of protocols could lead to the introduction of corner-cutting procedures that could put patients at risk. Lack of guidance or protocols can leave the practice open to criticism, at least, if an employee uses an unsafe procedure, or if disciplinary action is necessary.

For example, it is not enough to expect that a qualified nurse knows the current regulatory requirements for decontamination and infection control. Such an important responsibility should be properly recorded as a protocol and reviewed/revised regularly, often within the scope of guidance from the

PCT or Health Protection Agency Guidelines. Staff with the responsibility to undertake the task should know the protocol and in some organisations would be expected to sign a declaration that they had read, understood and would comply with it. The identified lead within the area should be enabled to remain up to date and to attend relevant training or study days. Any subsequent breach of compliance would be the subject of a counselling or disciplinary interview with the member of staff.

A practice might, however, decide that it did not need a protocol to ensure that administrative staff used an approved message of welcome when answering the telephone, particularly if staff turnover is low. In some communities patients and staff are neighbours, former school friends, or have become familiar with each other over many years. In these circumstances a written protocol would cause stilted conversations and a less happy atmosphere for both patients and staff.



## COUNSELLING UNDER-PERFORMING STAFF

It is usual for new members of staff to serve a probationary period, perhaps three months, before they are confirmed as permanent employees. This probationary period is of mutual benefit, allowing the employee to decide if he or she likes the work, his or her colleagues, the atmosphere in the practice, etc. For the practice it is an opportunity to decide if the employee matches expectations. Assuming each party is satisfied the practice should have a happy member of staff who will undertake tasks allocated responsibly.

After this time every member of staff should have at least an annual appraisal.

The questions to be asked by the practice manager if a member of staff is believed to be under-performing are:

- ‘what's gone wrong?’ It is not enough to assume that the fault lies with the employee
- has he or she been given tasks for which they have not been trained?
- is there a problem between members of staff? It is possible that an employee's supervisor has suddenly taken a personal dislike to him or her
- does the member of staff have personal problems? This can be particularly difficult if they are problems he or she would prefer not to discuss with a manager, e.g. health problems.

Normally a practice manager/partners would try to support a member of staff who is going through a bad patch. Pragmatically, good staff are difficult to recruit when rates of pay are not overly generous. Often staff stay in a practice out of loyalty to doctors and nurses with whom they enjoy working and for the prestige the job gives. Unless the member of staff is very new, the practice will have invested time and effort in training him or her and this investment should not be lightly ignored. Similarly the practice manager should not ignore the disruption, no matter how temporary, caused by having to recruit and train a new member of staff.

If the practice manager believes that the shortcoming rests with the employee, the issue must be addressed and quickly. Other staff will resent inaction if they believe the employee is not doing his or her fair share of work, or behaving in a way that reflects badly on them or the practice, e.g. an unhelpful attitude to patients at reception.

See p. 119 about the management of sickness absence, which could be a contributory factor to poor performance.

From this time onwards the practice manager must ensure that a formal, written procedure is followed closely, bearing in mind that at a future date his or her actions could be scrutinised by an employment tribunal.



Depending on how serious the issue is believed to be the practice manager might also consult the practice's solicitor.

The steps to be taken would normally be:

- **informal counselling** ○ at which time the practice manager will seek to identify the cause of any problem and, if possible, offer help. This session can be very helpful in resolving the issue if the member of staff is willing to discuss it. Even if he or she refuses to acknowledge that a problem exists it can sometimes be the catalyst to an acceptable improvement in performance
- **first disciplinary interview** ○ this might be the first discussion if the matter is serious, e.g. a flagrant breach of a written protocol. The employee would be advised in writing of the shortcoming and invited to attend the interview at a future date, perhaps a week ahead, and informed that he or she could be accompanied. Normally the practice manager would have someone attend the interview who could, if necessary, be called upon as a witness at an employment tribunal. The outcome, which could include a first written warning, would be recorded in a letter sent to the employee
- **second disciplinary interview** ○ if the employee's performance does not improve enough to satisfy the practice manager, he or she would be invited to attend a second interview. As for the first interview the reasons would be set down in writing and the employee could be accompanied. The outcome of this interview would depend on the progress, or lack of it, towards the required standard of work. If some progress had been made the practice manager, who would again

be accompanied, could decide to give the employee more time and support. Alternatively he or she could decide to terminate the member of staff's employment. The decision should be recorded in a letter sent to the employee.

## MANAGING SICKNESS ABSENCE

This can be challenging because malingering is difficult to prove. The practice should have a policy that requires any sickness to be reported to the member of staff's supervisor on the morning of the first day's absence. For clinicians this is particularly important because they will usually have patients booked to see them. All sickness, no matter how short in duration, should be recorded on an individual staff record. The act of recording the current sickness gives the manager the opportunity to review past sickness. Most sickness absences do not cause suspicion. However, it is reasonable to note a pattern. Is the member of staff always sick on the Friday before a bank holiday/annual leave? Or does he or she always experience sickness on two or three days a month. Other members of staff might drop hints, or even make direct accusations about an alleged abuse. Frequent short-term absences often point towards unhappiness or stress at home or at work rather than a severe or chronic disease.

If the sickness absences over a reasonable period of time suggest a problem the practice manager should first consider referring the member of staff to an occupational health department for independent assessment. Most members of staff will be more forthright with the occupational health department than they will with in-house colleagues. Many practices have agreed arrangements with the PCT or a local Acute Trust for an occupational health service. In such circumstances any further action would be delayed until a report had been received and considered. Sometimes the report will highlight an issue related to health and safety, e.g. the member of staff has back problems because the chair used does not provide adequate support. It is important that the practice addresses such a shortcoming because if the employee resigns he or she might claim compensation, or even unfair dismissal, on the grounds that the practice has not provided a safe place of work or adequate equipment for the employee to do his or her work.

### *PREVENTING LEGAL PROBLEMS*

Education and training and a good employment policy are essential in order to prevent stress, loss of safe practice and losing staff who might be able to claim against the practice for 'unfair dismissal' if they have not been adequately trained to do their work.

Regular appraisals, by the team lead, practice or office manager and/or one of the partners, provide the opportunity for any work-related problems to be discussed and addressed. Any such problems must be adequately recorded if the practice is to rely upon them in the event of a dispute or legal claim. It is essential that any action discussed with any member of staff whether of a positive or negative nature is recorded, with the date of the incident or event and any date for follow-up. Good (and confidential) recording in the case of staff records is as important as for patient records. Similarly allowing one partner to become familiar with employment law and good employment practice in addition to the practice manager will reduce the chances of the wrong advice being given or the wrong step taken 'in the heat of the moment'.



## DISMISSAL OF STAFF

If a practice is minded to dismiss a member of staff it is obliged to follow the statutory procedure, which is set out in full in Schedule 2 of the Employment Act 2002. The main steps can be summarised as follows:

### *STEP 1*

Write to the employee notifying them of what they are alleged to have done wrong – in terms of performance or conduct, set out the basis for the allegations, and invite him or her to a meeting to discuss the matter.

### *STEP 2*

Inform the employee of the grounds for making the allegations and hold a meeting to discuss them – at which the employee has the right to be accompanied. Notify the employee of the decision and the right to appeal.

### *STEP 3*

Hold an appeal meeting (if the employee wishes to appeal) at which the employee has the right to be accompanied – and inform the employee of the final decision.

These three steps are the legal minimum the practice must follow, but it would be advisable to follow the three stages of the procedure (counselling, first and second disciplinary interviews) explained in a previous paragraph unless the member of staff is accused of gross misconduct, for instance having put the health of a patient at serious risk, or attending to do clinical work under the influence of alcohol or drugs.

Dismissal should be a last resort in the management of staff. As stated earlier the practice will have invested time and effort in training him or her and this investment should not be lightly ignored. Similarly the practice manager should not ignore the disruption, no matter how temporary, caused by having to recruit and train a new member of staff.

ACAS has developed an electronic tool (*eManager*) to help employers deal with discipline and grievance situations in the workplace. It guides the employer through the necessary steps to be followed under the ACAS Code of Practice. It will help to ensure the actions taken are fair and appropriate. The system records all key decisions and actions, giving a permanent record of the procedures followed and records when and why decisions were taken.

Dismissal might not always be related to poor performance. Gross misconduct is conduct that justifies an employer in moving to the final stage of the disciplinary interview. Examples are dishonesty, assault of a patient or a colleague, or sexual harassment. Care needs to be taken with an accusation of gross misconduct and the member of staff should be given the opportunity to deny or offer any justification for the alleged action. The practice should also reflect on whether the scale of the conduct is sufficient to warrant it being regarded as gross misconduct. It is advisable to try to think as an employment tribunal might some months later.

*Redundancy* is also dismissal and a formal procedure should be followed that includes consultation with the member(s) of staff about the proposed redundancy. Redundancy pay is set out in a formula defined by statute. The practice needs to ensure that the criteria used to select the staff to be made redundant are carefully considered and formally recorded.

For entitlement to redundancy payments, under the Employment Rights Act 1996, redundancy arises when employees are dismissed because:

- the employer has ceased, or intends to cease, to carry on the business for the purposes of which the employee was so employed
- the employer has ceased, or intends to cease, to carry on the business in the place where the employee was so employed
- the requirements of the business for employees to carry out work of a particular kind has ceased or diminished or are expected to cease or diminish
- the requirements of the business for the employees to carry out work of a particular kind, in the place where they were so employed, has ceased or diminished or are expected to cease or diminish.

## Conclusion

It is important to get right the employment of staff. An appropriately employed member of staff who is supported and developed in his or her job and who works in a supportive team will contribute fully to the running of the organisation and the care of patients. Reviewing policies in the light of new legislation and reviewing the type and skill mix of the practice-employed workforce allows for the practice to be on a sound financial footing.

## Questions

1 ▷ When must a contract of employment be issued to a newly appointed member of staff?

2 ▷ Give three headings to be included in the contract of employment.

3 ▷ Give three examples of staff policies that must be available to all staff.

4 ▷ Are staff entitled to NHS rates of pay and conditions of service?

5 ▷ What staff are entitled to join the NHS superannuation scheme and what is the employer's percentage contribution for those who do?

6 ▷ What is a woman's entitlement to maternity leave and Statutory Maternity Pay?

7 ▷ What are the stages to follow if conducting disciplinary interviews?

8 ▷ What QoF targets include staff requirements?

9 ▷ What are the employer's duties under the Health and Safety at Work Act?

10 ▷ How often should a fire risk assessment be undertaken?

11 ▷ What national officer is responsible for the protection of personal information?

12 ▷ What proportion of the practice expenses might be spent on staff?

# Motivating and developing the team

# 8

*Hugh Flanagan*

### Scenario

*You have just joined a practice. The month before you start the practice manager invites you to a team-building day, as the practice is shortly to move into new premises and has merged with a neighbouring practice. The staff from the two practices know each other through general professional contacts but have not worked together in any close way. You wonder what is involved in a team-building day and what makes an effective team.*

*As part of your preparation for the day you have been given the following questions to consider and to prepare some brief notes as part of your contribution.*

- ▷ *What do you consider to be the purpose of the away day – what should be the outcomes?*
- ▷ *Given that this is a large practice, what and who do we mean by 'the team'?*
- ▷ *What might be the concerns of the team members and how might they be feeling?*
- ▷ *How would you like to see the team members working together, e.g. in terms of style of the meetings and the approach of the chair [how should the chair be selected?]?*

### Introduction

This chapter provides an introduction to understanding how to work in and help to develop an effective team. The focus is on 'a team' in the wider context of a practice. Some reference is made to the wider and related practice context and procedures, but the main focus is on the dynamics of a team of people who must integrate their work to achieve a particular task or tasks. (See Chapter 5 for a description of the make-up the primary healthcare team.)

It starts with a brief exploration of the definition and nature of 'a team' versus that of an organisation containing a number of teams. The next section draws on some of the research on teamworking in the NHS and is then followed by a discussion of the key features of effective teamworking with brief reference to research evidence and good practice in relation to each area, e.g. clarity of team objectives and goals, climate of openness and confronting difficulties/support and trust, task organisation, appropriate leadership and direction, and different team roles and behaviours.

The remaining sections deal with how to maintain and develop a team, and how to minimise the likelihood of conflict and to manage difficulties with team members.

The final section revisits the scenario with a short checklist of questions to encourage analysis of the scenario in more depth and gives some indicative answers.

---

## When is a team 'a team'?



What is the difference between a team and an organisation? This is partly an outcome of size and partly where one decides to draw the boundary in relation to a particular (multidisciplinary) service or professional/technical function or department.

A small practice of two or three GPs and a few support staff could be seen as one team with overlapping and complementary roles, with less demarcation or specialisation than would be found in a larger practice. The wider primary healthcare team will include GP partners, full and part time, salaried doctors, nursing and allied health professionals, and reception, ancillary and clerical staff. Some of these might be directly employed by the practice and some will be attached (for example district nurses and health visitors), i.e. their contract of employment might be held by the Primary Care Trust (PCT) or possibly by the local secondary care trust. There will also be other groups of stakeholders, such as Patient Participation Groups, which whilst not strictly part of the delivery team might be included as part of a wider team providing a patient perspective.

In larger practices there might be a number of 'teams' with different functions and responsibilities. Individuals might belong to a number of teams. For example, a partner GP will be part of, and have responsibilities in relation to, the overall practice management team but might also be a member of one or more clinical/service-oriented teams in conjunction with nursing, allied health professionals and clerical staff. There might be teams of receptionists or clinical teams (medical and nursing staff), the members of each functioning at times as part of one team and at others as part of another team.

The wider organisation provides the setting and context for a specific team and might or might not be conducive to effective teamworking. Issues that will affect this organisational context are how leadership is exercised, the impact this has on the culture of the organisation – 'the way we do things around here' – and whether this culture is one in which teams are enabled and encouraged to develop. For a general practice it is the partners who are accountable for leading the organisation, and they must do this taking into account both the internal needs of their organisation and the wider environment of primary and secondary care in which the practice exists.

In terms of this chapter we are examining the issues that relate to the development of a specific team in relation to the dynamics that contribute to effective teamworking.

---

## A review of some of the research on teams

### *The NHS context*



In the context of health care, working with others has long been recognised as an important feature of delivering patient care. In 1985, the Royal College of General Practitioners (RCGP) recommended primary care professionals should work more closely together, pooling their skills to improve patient care and personal job satisfaction. Two years later, in 1987, the Health Education Authority introduced a team-building training programme for primary care professionals. Since then the belief in the importance of teamworking skills to the success of healthcare delivery in the NHS has continued to grow.[1]

There is some limited evidence that multidisciplinary teamwork in primary care leads to reported improvements in health delivery and staff motivation,[2] and the better detection, treatment and follow-up and outcome in hypertension.[3] However, there is certainly room for improvement, with a study by West and Slater[4] reporting that less than one in four healthcare teams build effective communication and teamworking practices.

A major study in 2001 gathered questionnaire-based data from a large number of NHS teams in a variety of settings.[5] Their overall conclusion was that group processes, communication, clarity of objectives and leadership can all contribute to enhanced team effectiveness as well as promoting improved mental health in participants from effective teams. Well-run and diverse teams produce better innovation and quality of care, and both the leadership and culture of the organisational context in which the team(s) function are critical to the effectiveness of individual teams.

***The nature of teams***

Of the many definitions of teams two are offered below:

> [A] *distinguishable set of two or more people who interact dynamically, interdependently, and adaptively towards a common and valued goal/objective/mission, who each have been assigned specific roles or functions to perform, and who have a limited life-span of membership.*[6]

> [A] *small number of people with complementary skills who are committed to a common purpose, performance goals, and approach for which they hold themselves mutually accountable.*[7]

These two are included because they highlight the widely accepted criteria that define teamwork and distinguish it from merely working with others as a group. They also highlight the 'temporary' versus permanent nature of different teams – the limited-life project team versus the service delivery team.



In general practice most teams are likely to be permanent entities providing the working context for the professional life of many of its members. This not only places particular demands on the members of the team as individuals but also requires that considerable thought and action be given to developing the team to ensure it is effective. By 'effective' is meant that the team fulfils its purpose. It also needs to do this efficiently without wasting time and effort. Depending on the size of the practice and the team in question, 'purpose' might be defined as running the practice on a day-to-day basis, ensuring its long-term success or running a particular service within the practice.

Teams are also distinguished by the degree to which members work in a closely integrated way and/or in geographical proximity to each other. Obvious examples in health that illustrate the differences are operating theatre teams or resuscitation teams versus community mental health teams or midwifery teams. Within a practice it is important that individuals not only fulfil their individual roles effectively but also take responsibility for integrating their efforts with others in a supportive manner facilitated by effective communication.

A useful additional point to clarify is that a 'meeting' is not a team but a means by which teams, or representatives from different teams, communicate and do business. However, a team meeting is often a good place to observe the culture and characteristics of teams, either as a regular timed slot (see Chapter 9) or as an away day, as in the scenario at the start of the chapter. Teams need to learn how to run efficient meetings.

## The key features of effective teamworking

### *Do you need a team?*

The requirement for 'a team' depends on a number of factors including task complexity, the need for the integration of multiple skills and knowledge, speed such as in emergency situations, high volume and tight timescales. The requirement to reduce or prevent professional or social isolation among people doing individual jobs where there is minimal requirement to interact might also require the introduction of a team sense. So 'why' we need the team(s), its purpose and duration, and who needs to be part of it, are essential questions.

### *Task and process*



Clarity about the task – i.e. the particular thing the team has to do at any one time as well as the overarching purpose – is derived from the organisational or service context and dictates what process[es] the team needs in order to fulfil the task. Process is the mix of practical systems and methods used to get the job done plus what the team does to raise its performance and develop the skills and motivation of its members to interact effectively: to become an effective human group.

Task issues include:

- ▷ clarity about priorities and objectives
- ▷ how information is shared and used
- ▷ how decisions are made
- ▷ the methods and processes of communication both within the team and between the team and its wider constituency
- ▷ the conduct of team meetings including agenda-setting, time-keeping, participation and chairing.

Process issues include:

- ▷ how the team is led – autocracy versus democracy, shared leadership appropriate to the task
- ▷ how individuals contribute to the team both in terms of their professional role/knowledge and in terms of their style and behaviour
- ▷ how the team works together to achieve the task – a sense of mutual accountability: do members feel part of the team and able to give of their best?

### ***Team maturity***

Team development theory is concerned with describing the social processes that naturally occur when individuals work together. These might be seen as stages of group development where teams move through a set of phases, i.e.:[8,9]

- **forming** ○ the human group comes together and the predominant concerns are those of acceptance and place in the group, not the purpose and specific tasks of the team. At this stage leadership needs to be specific and directive of the process. The task is defined by the leader
- **storming** ○ not necessarily overt conflict but a process of clarification of task and process issues: agreeing the task and how we are going to work together, 'can I trust you', talkers versus listeners in the group, assertion of values and the need for performance outputs. The leader needs to allow and encourage exploration and questioning in this adolescent stage
- **norming** ○ ways of working that seem to be effective are established and begin to be applied. The team members understand the task and their contribution; they know each other and a sufficient degree of trust has been developed to enable effective communication. Leadership can now be less directive and more enabling
- **performing** ○ the mature team is working and this builds on the successful achievement of the task. Leadership becomes an enabling and facilitating role.



Teams need to be self-aware of their stage of development. The process of becoming a mature and effective team can be accelerated through regular review and reflection, and by taking the necessary maintenance and development actions. A significant change in the internal or external context of the team might affect the performance of even a mature, well-performing team. Examples might be a change in the organisational environment, an alteration in the task of the team or a new team member, all of which require work by the team to accommodate.

Despite the assumption that pooling of expertise should automatically result in enhanced performance, in practice interdisciplinary healthcare teams do not always work well.[10] Interpersonal conflict, communication blocks, low morale and poor performance frequently blight these teams. It is possible that the quality of patient care might be compromised (and an awareness of this might prevent problems occurring) in the early stages of team development, because only after passing through a sequence of development stages does the team reach a point where it is able to perform effectively.

Teams have to work at becoming and staying effective.

When considering the scenario one of the key objectives for the day would be how to maintain the team, and not assume that one away day will sort everything out.

### *Team decision-making*

A key feature of everyday teamwork is decision-making. What method is appropriate to the task of the team? Teams need to decide how they will make decisions in the variety of circumstances that the team and its individual members will meet. An obvious example would be an operating department team deciding on how decisions will be made in certain critical or emergency situations that might be anticipated in a particular procedure. The process in the team meeting where these matters are being discussed prospectively might be quite open and democratic. However, once in an actual emergency, decision-making is likely to be autocratic and directive. In community mental health or palliative care, decision-making is likely to be characterised by more consultation and discussion at most stages of the treatment pathway.

Observing team meetings is a good way of identifying the overall cultural norm of the team in relation to how it makes decisions. Some of the more obvious ways in which teams make decisions are:

- **lack of response** ○ the 'plop' or lead balloon approach where no one responds to or builds on ideas – the team lacks motivation or the team members tend not to listen to each other (the distinction between active and passive listening)?
- **authority rule** ○ the person in the chair makes the decisions – a substitute for personal commitment by team members or the preferred style of the leader who is also the chair?
- **minority rule** ○ railroading, intimidating, fixing – the team is not particularly cohesive and different factions and individuals are intent on pursuing their own agendas rather than the teams?
- **majority rule** ○ voting/polling – an illustration of efficient democracy in action or a lazy way of avoiding working through differences, resulting in 'lowest common denominator decisions'?
- **consensus** ○ everyone has his or her say, and differences are seen as helpful and are worked through until a decision is reached that everyone will commit to and support. Such decisions hold up under external scrutiny and pressure – probably the most effective form of decision-making but one that requires focused and efficient teamworking and trust between team members

- **unanimity** – 'groupthink' – might be the result of well-developed teamworking and shared values, but might result from a lack of critical faculty and reflection, and should be treated with suspicion if it becomes the norm?

### *Team roles – being an effective team member*

Much of the current thinking about how to be an effective team member centres on the idea of preferred team roles. A major influence upon this type of thinking and probably one of the best known is the work of Belbin who over many years has proposed and investigated eight team roles.[11,12] These are differentiated from work roles.

Belbin defines a team role as 'Our tendency to behave, contribute and interrelate with others in a particular way.' In contrast, a work role is defined as 'The mix of tasks and responsibilities undertaken by individuals or within a team.'



Table 8.1 ○ ***Belbin team roles***

| Team role | Contribution to the team | Allowable weaknesses |
|---|---|---|
| Plant | Creative, solves difficult problems, independent outlook | Loses touch with everyday realities? |
| Resource Investigator | Enterprising, quick to explore new opportunities | Weak in follow-through? |
| Co-ordinator/Chair | Makes good use of group activities and team members, good communicator | Manipulative? |
| Shaper | Thrusting, challenging, pushes group | Provocative, aggressive, intolerant? |
| Monitor/Evaluator | Critical thinking ability, discerning, objective | Hypercritical, uninspiring, sceptical? |
| Teamworker | Co-operative, averts friction, aware of underlying feelings in team | Indecisive? |
| Implementer/Company Worker | Organised, efficient, practical | Slow to see new possibilities? |
| Completer/Finisher | Painstaking, conscientious, deadline-aware | Anxious, reluctant to delegate? |

Another fairly well-known piece of work is that of Margerison and McCann who have introduced the Management Team Wheel, which also describes eight alternative roles (i.e. Explorer/Promoter, Assessor/Developer, Thruster/Organiser, Concluder/Producer, Controller/Inspector, Upholder/Maintainer, Reporter/Adviser and Creator/Innovator).[13]

Both of these approaches ask individuals to express their preferences for particular roles on the basis that in the preferred role people will contribute to the team at an enhanced level, rather than if forced to participate in a less preferred role. The underlying model is that a team needs all of the roles in order to function effectively and that an absence or imbalance will lead to less than optimal functioning.

The effectiveness of team members is considerably enhanced if they have self-insight into the impact of their behaviour on the work of the team. Knowing the preferences of other team members facilitates communication and understanding of different approaches. Team members can share the leadership of the team by consciously using their strengths to help the team at particular junctures as the team works through problems.



## Maintaining and developing a team

There is a lot of evidence to show that teams don't always give attention to how they work, particularly if things seem to be generally alright. But underlying feelings of things not being quite right or not really feeling part of the team can become critical when the team is put under pressure. Fault lines are exposed and might cause the team to break apart. Teams don't just happen; they need maintenance and development. This can often be the case when the pressure is on to manage an increasing case load in primary care, or when a multitude of government initiatives cascade down upon a practice and its team.

Numerous studies highlight the importance of a team climate that is characterised by interpersonal trust and mutual respect, where team members are comfortable being themselves and are confident that they will not be embarrassed, rejected or punished for behaviours such as airing differences or handling confrontations. Both the quality and quantity of team communication appears to be determined by these issues of 'psychological safety'.[14]

The organisational context in which teams operate might have as much to do with their success as their internal operations, i.e. does the context facilitate and reward teamworking?

As is apparent from the definitions of a team above, all team members are mutually accountable for the success of the team. There will usually be someone who is the formal leader, or *primus inter pares*, in the team. In terms of maximising the effective leadership of teams the following points should be considered:

1 ▷ ensuring clarity regarding purpose, context and specific tasks – yours and the team's

2 ▷ communicating this constantly within the team, and between the team and the rest of the organisation

3 ▷ knowing your team members – who can be left to get on with it, and who needs more direction and support; knowing when you need to adapt your approach

4 ▷ balancing directing with empowering the team

5 ▷ ensuring review and reflection on performance

6 ▷ giving time and attention to developing the team.



Similarly, being an effective player in the team is maximised by adopting the following as the basis of your approach to the team:

1 ▷ ensuring you understand purpose, context and specific tasks of the team

2 ▷ knowing and communicating your role and particular contribution

3 ▷ proactive contribution plus enabling the same from others

4 ▷ sharing responsibility for the team performance and development

5 ▷ supporting whilst challenging to ensure different views get heard

6 ▷ encouraging review, reflection and development.

---

## Managing the difficult team member

### *Why are people difficult?*

Why do some people seem to be natural team players and others not? It might be an aspect of personality, i.e. some of us prefer to just do our thing and to leave others to do theirs, but nevertheless if we are part of the team we can all learn to become more effective team players if we want to. We often perceive others as difficult simply because they are different from us, and there is no mechanism or opportunity for bridging this – we can improve this situation by putting into practice some of the guidance in this chapter.

On the other hand, some people might lack the motivation to integrate, to support and work with others, or indulge in behaviour that is disruptive or unpleasant and are unwilling to change. This would be dealt with by a different process that could lead ultimately to action under a disciplinary procedure, which is not the subject of this chapter. Of course, before overly reacting to a difficult individual we need to consider whether there is a consistent pattern of behaviour over time or whether it is episodic or occasional, and possibly associated with some non-work situation, e.g. responsibilities as a carer. We can all have an off-day and be difficult on occasions; what should be a matter of concern is the existence of a pattern of behaviour.

So the first question is 'Are we perceiving others as difficult simply because there is no process for examining how the team members work together utilising the differences in approach to enhance and enrich the work of the team?' A first step might be to use the Belbin team roles referred to on p. 130 to clarify and then explore the impact of individual differences, and how these can work together to maximise team performance.



Sometimes tensions arise because teams simply do not give time and attention to the human needs of the group or people who are 'the team'. We assume everyone in 'the team' recognises that they are part of 'the team' and not just an individual who happens to talk to others from time to time and attends 'the team' meeting. Is there a binding sense of common purpose?

As illustrated above we all have different preferences for how we work in a team, our team roles. We also have different ways of problem-solving and approach the process of defining and analysing problems differently, with some of us preferring highly structured approaches and others much looser 'out of the box' approaches. These differences can be explored using appropriate psychometrics such as the Adaption-Innovation Inventory.[15] Wider differences in personality type can be explored using an instrument such as the Myers–Briggs Type Inventory.[16]

This diversity of approaches can lead to mutual incomprehension, if not outright hostility, if it is not understood, valued and used for the benefit of the team. Different tasks and circumstances require different skills and ways of thinking. So a key aspect of reducing the likelihood of 'difficult' team members is to give time to meaningful exploration of the individual and collective skills, and characteristics of the team, through structured time-out or away days, as well as opportunities for social interaction, outside of the day-to-day business agenda.

### *Organisational context?*

The first thing to consider is whether a sense of 'teamness' is part of the overall practice (organisational) culture, 'the way "we" do things around here'. Ultimately the performance of any practice is dependent on the culture of the senior team and its effectiveness. Is there an explicit sense of common purpose that is communicated to the rest of the practice backed up by clear direction, support and visible action? This is in effect the preventive strategy, i.e. providing an environment within the practice that minimises the likelihood of difficult behaviour occurring. Basically, is the practice one that is managed and led? The larger the practice the more explicit leadership and management need to be.

However, if a member of the practice is deliberately disruptive or fails to heed, or is blind to, normal feedback on the effects of his or her behaviour, then as mentioned above it falls to the senior team to have in place a process for managing this in order to prevent destructive conflict affecting performance. Being seen to take effective action in such matters both affects and helps to establish the culture of the practice – the way we do things around here.



Other related features of practice management would be the proactive development of individuals through an effective Personal Development Planning process and the integration of that process with wider practice objectives and processes including the Practice Professional Development Plan, i.e. are the different processes in harmony with each other in terms of their intentions and execution?

### *Team maturity?*

In terms of the stages of development, is the team a mature team, i.e. has it gone through a process of 'storming' and 'norming' in order to achieve effective performance or is it still stuck in the 'forming' stage? This can sometimes be the case even after a number of years if nothing has been done to develop the team. The essential nature of human differences, of personality and style, of life experience and background, of training, of perceptions and assumptions all provide a basis for conflict based on misunderstanding, if they are not shared and understood through effective dialogue and interpersonal and intra-team communication.

The culture or climate within a team needs to be consciously fostered through leadership and through challenge, from all team members, to any behaviour that is destructive of the team's ethos.

### *Individual motivation and needs*

Understanding what motivates people is helpful in considering whether the organisation – the practice overall – is sensitive to and able to meet the legitimate needs of its members. There are various theories and models of motivation such as the well-known 'hierarchy of needs' developed by Abraham Maslow and subsequently refined.[17] This postulates that until certain basic needs are met then higher-level needs and actions will take a back seat. For example, Maslow states that there are five basic levels of human need:

- basic biological and physiological needs, such as food and shelter
- safety needs, such as security, protection, law and stability
- social 'belongingness' and affiliation, such as relationships, work group, affection
- a need for esteem derived from achievement, status, recognition
- 'self-actualisation', enabled once the previous four levels of need are met, derived from the opportunity for personal growth and fulfilment.



These five levels can be related to different organisational features. For example, biological and physiological needs are met by paying a living wage so that an individual has the opportunity to purchase these requirements, followed by a stable and ordered work environment that promotes physical and mental security. Next comes the sense of belonging and identity, with the organisation promoted by its leadership style, the values that underpin the way staff are managed, and the differences between people. This leads to the fourth level in terms of the way it gives recognition for achievement and responsibility, and provides status and a sense of self-worth to the people that work in it. The final and fifth stage of self-actualisation, a sense of personal growth and fulfilment, can be met in part by the opportunities provided within and by the practice, but might also be found outside the immediate work context through professional pursuits in the wider world or other non-work-related opportunities that the individual finds fulfilling.

What motivates and drives a newly arrived female GP of 33 is likely to be different in many respects from that which drives a male GP of 55, or a practice nurse of 40. Similarly, the expectations and perceptions of the practice owners will be different from those of a part-time, unskilled employee.

### *Taking action*

Where a team has arrived at a position where there are difficulties with and between members, assuming the team has worked at developing itself, nothing will change unless and until 'the team', or a majority of its members, are willing to confront the perceived difficulties or the difficult person. Where there is a formal leader of the team, or a *primus inter pares*, the responsibility for initiating action usually lies with him or her. This might initially be quite informal and might reveal simply that an individual was unaware of the impact of his or her behaviour or approach and, once aware, the behaviour is modified. However, if as mentioned above he or she fails to respond to this, then action might need to be taken under a more formal disciplinary process.

## The scenario

Returning to the scenario we can now pose a further series of questions to analyse the situation in more depth. The new member of the team could arrive with the following questions to help structure the time-out event and develop the effectiveness of the team:



- ▷ how clear are we about the purpose and objectives of the team and the particular task(s) on the table at any one time?
- ▷ is the way the team organises and structures itself suitable for the task(s) we undertake?
- ▷ how is the information necessary for the team to undertake its task(s) obtained and used?
- ▷ is our decision-making effective and are our methods/techniques appropriate?
- ▷ does everyone participate fully?
- ▷ is leadership exercised appropriately?
- ▷ are feelings and opinions expressed openly?
- ▷ do we use our time in meetings well?
- ▷ do we enjoy working in this team?
- ▷ do we know something of our own preferred style and approach in teamworking, and how this fits with the rest of the team members?

## Questions

**1** ▷ How do you define a team?

**2** ▷ When might you need a team?

**3** ▷ What are team roles?

4 ▷ Are these the same as work roles?

5 ▷ What team roles were suggested by Belbin?

6 ▷ What processes will a team go through?

7 ▷ Why is a meeting not a team?

**References**

1 • Cook R. Paths to effective teamwork in primary care settings *Nursing Times* 1996; **92(14)**: 44–5.

2 • Wood N, Farrow S, Elliott B. A review of primary health care organisations *Journal of Clinical Nursing* 1994; **3(4)**: 243–50.

3 • Adorion D, Silverberg D S, Tomer D, *et al.* Group discussion with the health care team: a method of improving care of hypertension in general practice *Journal of Human Hypertension* 1990; **4(3)**: 265–8.

4 • West M A, Slater J A. *The Effectiveness of Team Working in Primary Health Care* London: Health Education Authority, 1996.

5 • Borrill C S, Carletta J, Carter A J, *et al. The Effectiveness of Health Care Teams in the National Health Service* Aston Centre for Health Service Organization Research, University of Aston; Human Communications Research Centre, Universities of Glasgow and Edinburgh; Psychological Therapies Research Centre, University of Leeds, 2001.

6 • Salas E, Dickinson T L, Converse S A, *et al.* Towards an understanding of team performance and training. In: R W Swezey, E Salas (eds). *Teams: their training and performance* Norwood, NJ: Ablex Publishing Corporation, 1992, pp. 3–29.

7 • Katzenbach J R, Smith D X. *The Wisdom of Teams* New York: McKinsey & Company, 1993.

8 • Tuckman B W. Developmental sequence in small groups *Psychological Bulletin* 1965; **63**: 384–99.

9 • Tuckman B W, Jensen M A. Stages of small group development revisited *Group and Organization Studies* 1977; **2(4)**: 419–27.

10 • Farrell M P, Schmitt M H, Heinemann G D. Informal roles and the stages of interdisciplinary team development *Journal of Interprofessional Care* 2001; **15(3)**: 281–95.

11 • Belbin R M. *Management Teams: why they succeed or fail* (second edn) Oxford: Butterworth-Heinemann, 2004.

12 • Belbin R M. *Team Roles at Work* Oxford: Butterworth-Heinemann Ltd, 1993.

13 • Margerison C J, McCann D J. *Team Management: practical new approaches* London: Mercury Business Guides, 1995.

14 • Dyer W G. *Team Building: current issues and new alternatives* Wokingham, UK: Addison-Wesley, 1999.

15 • Kirton M J. *Adaption-Innovation: in the context of diversity and change* Hove, East Sussex: Routledge, 2006.

16 • Briggs-Myers I, McCaulley MH, Quenk NL, *et al. MBTI Manual: a guide to the development and use of the Myers–Briggs Type Indicator* Palo Alto, CA: Consulting Psychologists Press, 1998.

17 • Maslow A. A theory of human motivation *Psychological Review* 1943; **50**: 370–96.

# Organising and running a meeting

# 9

*Robert Cragg*

### *Scenario*

*You are a partner in a practice. You have been tasked with establishing a regular meeting to ensure the surgery adheres to the GP contract requirements, following last year's disappointing performance against the Quality and Outcomes Framework (QoF) criteria. You have been asked to look at leading the first of these forums. You must decide when the practice will hold these meetings and how often, identifying who should attend and deciding what terms of reference and agenda items this forum will follow.*



## Introduction

Love them or loathe them organisations need meetings to fulfil essential roles of: communication, decision-making, monitoring, problem-solving, debate and development.[1]

It's a typical cliché that the NHS always holds too many 'meetings'; the mere mention of the word can invoke cynicism amongst the majority of frontline staff. We can all identify with this opinion, as we have all attended meetings that are either poorly prepared and led or that have complex agenda items brushed aside or left to remain unresolved. This should not and need not be the case if basic, fundamental principles of holding and running meetings are followed. This chapter does not aim to give all the answers but aims to break down the key components and structure that will enable meetings to be successful in achieving their stated objectives.

## Justifying a meeting

The first criterion vital for success is having a *valid reason to call a meeting*. Too often meetings occur for issues that could be resolved by a group email or a few quick phone calls. The crux of any requirement for a meeting is the need for consultation or debate, when a two-way, face-to-face communication is essential to achieve objectives and give staff an opportunity to make a contribution.[1]

A meeting about an issue involving several members of the practice would help to discuss and solve problems, allowing attendees to collectively identify ways to improve performance against identified criteria. Face-to-face communications can also be key to motivate staff to change their current practice and feel part of any implemented changes.

## Frequency of meetings

Meetings vary in their formality, duration and size. Meetings can be held as a series of events or a more simple 'one off' occasion. Running regular meetings to monitor progress against certain targets might require frequency to ensure improvements are being made, but beware, as running the same meeting on a long-term, regular basis on the premise that agenda items will emerge can lead to bad practice and be inefficient. Those attending recurrent periodic meetings can lose their vision and effectiveness, with familiarity breeding complacency.[2,3] Meetings should be deployed dynamically, according to when decisions or consultation are required.



## Meeting membership

Once the purpose and frequency of a meeting has been established it is important to decide who should attend, ensuring you obtain membership at the meeting comprising delegates from all staff groups for whom the meeting's actions will affect, being careful to balance inclusiveness with practicality.[4]

If too many people attend, discussions generally become too protracted, conversely too few, and changes appear imposed rather than mutually agreed. When there is a choice over who can attend, try to select people with a positive outlook and constructive disposition, over those who are negative and destructive.

The membership of a meeting should include all the people with the desired expertise required to contribute and make the necessary decisions. Sometimes achieving a comprehensive list of essential delegates inevitably means that not all the attendees will be 'dynamic' or even 'constructive', but might be needed because of their position or expertise. How to manage such individuals is discussed later in the chapter.

Always consider if all people have to be in the meeting for the whole duration. If someone is popping in to give specialist support to one part of the agenda there is no need for them to sit though the entire meeting.[1] This is often useful in a busy clinical practice, and avoids the unnecessary loss of patient contact time.

When looking at the scenario at the start of the chapter, key personnel involved in the monitoring of chronic disease targets would need to be invited or represented. This can include principal GPs, practice and district nurse representatives, individuals with IT and financial responsibility, as well as key staff members, from administration involved in the call and recall of patients. When thinking about the scenario, you might initially decide to run a series of separate meetings with wide stakeholder coverage, to generate issues and ideas linked to QoF performance. Latterly you might then wish to break up the stakeholders into separate subgroups to look at specific areas in detail (see Chapter 15). Operating a central project board with supportive input from the lead of each subgroup could be an effective way to manage the workload within the scenario provided.



## Timing and venue

Once the membership is decided, the work and social commitments of the members should be accounted for as far as possible, scheduling meeting dates that don't clash with the school run or holiday periods, with coverage of all key staff. Adjourning or recalling a meeting because key people are absent is wasteful.[5]

Meetings before lunch and before the close of play can focus the mind, with participants tending to be less concerned with chatter and anecdotes, although care should be taken not to set too short a time and thus risk overlapping with surgery and clinic start times. Meetings need to keep time, with start and finish times strictly honoured. Special dispensation to the late minority will frustrate the punctual majority. It is worth remembering that every minute spent on meetings diverts resources and time from frontline care, at the cost of patients and cost to the practice.

Meetings legitimately fulfil a social function. If applicable, it is important to account for team bonding by building in time at the beginning or end of the meeting to ensure socialising doesn't encroach on the core business of the meeting. Venues must be comfortable but not too comfortable, free from distraction and on neutral ground.[3,4]

When considering the scenario at the start, it might be worth investing dedicated time out with an away day 'off site' to focus in detail on the subject matter. Subsequent meetings might be best placed within the practice for ease of access.

## Preparing for a meeting

Successful meetings are reliant on impeccable pre-planning and preparation, with a clear purpose and specific objectives. Agenda-setting is critical, defining what will be covered within the meeting. The clearer and more focused the agenda items, the more likely the meeting will meet its objectives.

## The agenda



All meetings centre on an agenda, which is essential to structure and focus a meeting.[1] A good agenda should:

- ideally be formed in advance with all stakeholders having an opportunity to contribute to it
- be ordered in a logical sequence detailing who will be accountable for leading each component on the agenda
- be balanced with the scope of the agenda in accordance with its duration; for instance, key items should be placed high up the agenda to ensure adequate time and attention is provided, with delegates retaining full concentration
- detail the provisional length of time each agenda item will be allocated for discussion
- ensure large agenda items are broken down into smaller items. This allows the delegates at the meeting to focus on particular areas, whilst not losing sight of the overall subject matter. Care should always be taken for items not to be presented in a way that apportions blame on a member of the meeting, as this can hinder resolution of a problem
- where appropriate continuity to the previous meeting should be referenced.[4] Include formalities such as the date, time and apologies.

## Preparing to attend

A delegate attending a meeting needs prior preparation, to define what he or she wishes to say and consider how best to put his or her point forward. If there is a contentious issue, it is wise to pre-empt how others attending the meeting will react and respond, thinking through any counter-arguments carefully. Rehearsing and investigating the potential position and perspective of others enables you to pre-empt any difficult questions. Any stated position will need to be believable, consistent and backed up with evidence. Being prepared can help a delegate to be:

- ▷ succinct
- ▷ persuasive
- ▷ precise
- ▷ timely in delivering a key message

and to

- ▷ use clear language
- ▷ avoid the use of jargon.[1]



Conversely poor preparation can result in an inability to have influence during the debate.

In the meeting itself a delegate should have all the facts and figures linked to that area of work to hand. Speculating on what the figures 'might be' causes unnecessary challenge and debate. The accuracy of information presented at the meeting is paramount and should have been fully researched in advance, otherwise the agenda item risks being postponed and tabled again at a future meeting. It is useful to consider the presentation of any data, and review whether a formal report or visual aids are required.

---

## Meeting roles and the position of the chair

Meetings work when all stakeholders and the chair know their role and unique contribution. Within the meeting, roles need to be assigned. All meetings require a chair and a scribe, preferably both as 'independent' as possible. The 'scribe' should be someone who is able to accurately take notes and transpose the notes into clear minutes that summarise the important points of the meeting. Ideally the scribe should be someone who does not necessarily need to be involved in the discussion of the meeting.

The choice of who is to chair the meeting is critical. *'Chairs'* need not be the most senior member of the team, but require skills and stakeholder respect sufficient to direct the meeting. They should be consistent, when several meetings are intended to provide continuity. The chair should have a positive demeanour establishing the right tone for the type of meeting being run; for example, meetings on cost-cutting will require a different ambience from those on acquiring new investments. The chairman or chairwoman has the following principal roles.

### Remaining focused

- Strictly follow the agenda items prescribed, keeping all participants focused on the subject in hand.
- Avoid digressions or tackling new, independent issues that have been brought to the table.
- Ensure the objectives of the meeting are being achieved.
- It is vital to maintain the enthusiastic involvement of all stakeholders. Chairs must retain delegates' full attention at all times.
- Attentiveness is essential, so 'chairs' need to listen and observe how people are responding to the debate.



### Making delegates feel at ease

- Be encouraging.
- Make people comfortable. Meetings can be intimidating places for some stakeholders – perform introductions and coax involvement from those who are too timid to engage due to issues like lack of seniority, shyness or nerves.
- Be positive – working in a successful meeting can be a motivational experience, whereas coming out of a dysfunctional meeting can sap your enthusiasm for work. People must be encouraged to leave cynicism behind at the door of the meeting and arrive with a common belief that the meeting will be successful.

### Controlling the flow of conversation

- Ensure discussion is prompted in an open and fair manner, considering all stakeholder perspectives, with just one delegate speaking at any given time.
- The chair must see that conversation is equitably shared amongst the group, avoiding dominant individuals railroading the meeting.
- Each representative of the meeting should be treated as an equal, and, whilst being mindful of social hierarchies, seniors should not dominate proceedings.
- You must respond and adapt your chairing style with the mood of the meeting.

### Being fair

- ▷ Remain neutral and open-minded.
- ▷ Enable everyone to participate.

### Invoking creativity

- ▷ Inspire creative thinking through open questions. Encourage the development of a novel viewpoint or alternative solution if the meeting becomes stale.

### Ensuring confidentiality

- ▷ Allow sensitive issues to be discussed in a safe and open manner, ensuring that patient information is confidential and all participants feel 'safe' to express their views.



### House-keeping duties

- ▷ To ensure the meeting runs to time.
- ▷ Take responsibility for pre- and post-meeting communications.
- ▷ Be the central figure of knowledge and reference points.

### Retaining order

- ▷ Establish and ensure the group upholds the ground rules for behaviour.
- ▷ A commonly overlooked element of the chair's role is to control the emotional content of meetings. Debates and decisions have an emotive content, which the chair needs to explore without allowing individual stakeholders to be left exposed. If an individual is allowed to become too emotional it can prove too contentious, divisive and disruptive.
- ▷ Inspire compromise where necessary.

### Providing clarity

- ▷ Clarify people's understanding of both the meeting content and of key decisions made.
- ▷ Summarise the discussions and ensure all people are signed up to agreements and actions before the meeting adjourns.
- ▷ Establish who will action agreed items of work – establishing deadlines as required.[1,2,5]

## Handling 'problem' delegates

Different problematic personalities can be a challenge to the productivity of a meeting and thus need to be proactively managed. At extremes, delegates can talk incessantly, override conversations, or can be apathetic or dismissive of all ideas. People can, and unfortunately do, arrive at meetings with grievances, underhand motives or intimidating behaviour.[1] Rivalries can exist both within teams and, especially, across teams and between practices, and all of these can become apparent or come to a head in a meeting. Irrespective of an individual's apparent altruistic exterior, everybody attending a meeting has his or her own individual motivations, hidden alliances and preferred outcomes. Having someone who effectively chairs the meeting can minimise these sort of problems, but all participants have a shared responsibility to constructively minimise disruptive behaviour.

When problems between individuals arise intervention is essential. Tactics might include:



- ▷ breaking up the flow of conversation and politely interjecting, which might be appropriate strategies for those who 'waffle' or simply like the sound of their own voice
- ▷ asking questions to seek involvement of the quieter or overlooked individuals
- ▷ using prior knowledge of relevant experiences of key members of the team to prompt a request for information, thus encouraging the perspective of someone who is unable to contribute easily
- ▷ if comments appear persistently negative, asking the perpetrators if they think their contribution is being constructive to the meeting. (This can be done after or even during a meeting.) This might allow pause for reflection, especially if this is done in an assertive but not an aggressive way
- ▷ similarly asking those who can only find problems with others' suggestions if they can suggest a solution of their own
- ▷ at the extreme – isolation or expelling an individual with a polite explanation, which might be required if behaviour is such that the meeting is unable to proceed.

## Following meetings through

A meeting's success is judged by what happens after its completion, by the results of its impact at the front line, be that the dissemination of information or the enactment of major service redesign. Information from meetings needs to be sent out rapidly in order to sustain momentum of agreed changes and aid frontline credibility for the forum in question.

*Minutes* are essential for ensuring delegates have a clear record of what was discussed and agreed. They disseminate information to colleagues as well as acting as an official record. An agreed record of what is said is essential and prevents meeting outcomes being distorted by 'Chinese whispers'. Minutes do not have to be a verbatim account, but must:

- ▷ contain truthful and unbiased content
- ▷ be jargon free
- ▷ be short and snappy.

In the NHS increasing scrutiny and freedom of information means that minutes are increasingly held as accurate records in the public domain.[2,4]

Sending minutes out to all is not always strictly essential *but* if no follow-through is performed it can result in inaction. Too often delegates will only perform their given task once prompted to do so. They need not be disseminated as a 'hard copy'– emailed reminders and attachments are a great paperless means of communicating outcomes.

Minutes should follow a standardised format typically following a house style evolved within our organisations. Irrespective of the specific layout the key criteria that should emerge from the document are four-fold:

1. ▷ what decisions have been made
2. ▷ what action has been agreed to be taken
3. ▷ who is taking responsibility for enactment
4. ▷ what are the deadlines for this work to be completed.[1]

---

## Avoid meeting overload

All primary care team members lead busy lives, so not only should the decision to call a meeting be thought through carefully, but also the decision to attend a meeting. It is always important when making the latter decision to try and think through what the consequences of not attending might be in the widest sense. For instance, non-attendance at a PCT meeting might result in your practice being unaware of the reasons behind a decision that later affects you, or persistently not attending (and being the only practice to do this) may set up communication difficulties with the PCT. This is turn may make the practice appear difficult or unengaged, when it might be merely very busy.

Attendance at meetings should be a two-way process; in return for your contribution you should get something in return (this need not be financial!), for instance an increase in knowledge, or influence on a service redesign. A balance should be struck between attending meetings, communication and the work you are employed to perform.

| Box 9.1 ○ ***Ten top tips for a successful meeting*** |
|---|
| 1 • Preparation. |
| 2 • Purpose. |
| 3 • Time scheduling. |
| 4 • Create understanding. |
| 5 • Staying on track. |
| 6 • Use diverse experience and skills. |
| 7 • Creative problem-solving. |
| 8 • Check for agreement. |
| 9 • Review the working of the team. |
| 10 • Action. |
| *Source*: Briner, Hastings and Geddes.[6] |



## Conclusion

Effective meetings can, with the collective effort and contribution of its delegates, be highly productive, and have a central role in creating organisational change.

Meeting participants need to:

- ▷ prepare in advance
- ▷ communicate and discuss issues responsibly and professionally
- ▷ think about the roles and behaviour of all the delegates or participants
- ▷ follow through any agreed actions
- ▷ consider the perception and position of all stakeholders, not only those present at the meeting
- ▷ think carefully whether a meeting is needed, or if their attendance is needed
- ▷ consider the effect their non-attendance will have on those around them if unsure whether to attend, both at the place of work and in the

local NHS as a whole.

If this sounds unrealistic it might be necessary to change the culture and organisation of meetings in your organisation, to become more proficient and credible.

Finally, meetings must not replace or be an alternative for day-to-day problem-solving and should not replace informal consultations and communications within the team. The majority of clinical and management change in a practice needs to evolve through the immediacy of informal contacts.

## Questions

**1** ▷ What justifies a meeting?

**2** ▷ How often should the meeting run?

**3** ▷ Who should attend?

**4** ▷ When and where should the meeting be held?

**5** ▷ What prior preparation needs to be completed?

**6** ▷ What key roles need to be allocated for a meeting to run smoothly?

**7** ▷ What are the responsibilities of a chair?

**8** ▷ How can you deal with difficult delegates?

**9** ▷ What are the essential features of meeting minutes?

**10** ▷ What are the ten top tips for running a successful meeting?



### References

1 • Forsyth P. *Making Meetings Work* (Management Shaper series) London: The Chartered Institute of Personnel and Development, 1996.

2 • Timm P. *How to Hold Successful Meetings: 30 action tips for managing effective meetings* Franklin Lakes, NJ: Career Press, 1997.

3 • Friedmann S. *Meeting and Event Planning for Dummies* Hoboken, NJ: Wiley, 2003.

4 • Heller R, Hindle T. *Essential Managers: managing meetings* London: Dorling Kindersley, 1998.

5 • Institute of Leadership and Management. *Effective Meetings at Work* (fourth edn) Oxford: Pergamon Open Learning, 2003.

6 • Briner W, Hastings C, Geddes M. *Project Leadership* (second edn) Aldershot: Gower, 1996.

# The GP as a leader

# 10

*Peter Spurgeon*

### *Scenario*

*Your practice needs to determine its approach to Practice-Based Commissioning (PBC) and a meeting of all staff has been called to discuss it. An approach from another local practice, already very active in commissioning, has been received about collaboration. However, there is some level of historical resentment towards this practice and scepticism about their motives. Equally there are varying views within the practice about the new commissioning situation; with those doctors who took part in fundholding in the past being enthusiastic, through to the practice manager's anxiety about the procedures and bureaucracy that may develop in working with the Primary Care Trust (PCT). You have been asked to take the lead in the meeting and for the future commissioning.*



## Introduction

The challenge of delivering health care is in itself increasingly complex, with increasing advances in medical knowledge and techniques reaching unprecedented rates. In addition practitioners face a more fragmented and complicated series of policies from above, with escalating expectations from both politicians and patients. This is in addition to a wider range of provider organisations and networks, and continued structural and system changes.

Traditionally healthcare organisations like those of primary care had fairly predictable patterns of work and behaviour, with clear hierarchical structures and stable environments. Change, when it happened, tended to be evolutionary rather than radical. Increasingly over the last 10 years new and emerging healthcare organisations have greater fluidity of roles and overlapping of boundaries with other agencies.[1] Writing in the *British Medical Journal* Plesk and Greenhalgh[2] conclude that:

> *To cope with escalating complexity in health care we must abandon linear models, accept unpredictability, respect (and utilise) autonomy and creativity, and respond flexibly to emerging patterns and opportunities.*

In parallel to the change there has been a gradual increased emphasis on leadership over management. Whether management or leadership is more important can lead to confusion, especially where to separate and distinguish completely the roles of leaders and managers, is overly simplistic. The nature of the task will determine whether a leadership or management approach has greater primacy and where the need to move from one to the other, or blend the two, becomes necessary.

---

## Clinical leadership and clinical management

At its most polarised the debate about leadership and management has tended to see leadership as 'good' and management as 'bad'. As Grint suggests the origins of the word 'management' are to do with control, often associated with a bureaucratic structure and therefore not viewed as especially attractive.[3] In contrast the term 'leadership' is linked to providing direction. This is a more optimistic and future-oriented concept with leaders offering guidance towards a better situation, and therefore can be a rather more appealing concept.



A classic, possibly stereotypical view is of the manager as being:

- primarily administrative
- working to a short-term perspective
- within the current systems and structures.

The focus is upon making that which exists as efficient as possible.

In contrast the leader:

- takes a longer-term perspective
- seeks to initiate change for the better
- interests and inspires people to commit to a 'vision of what the organisation could be like'.[4]

The basic management tasks such as planning, budgeting and organising are vital to the smooth running of any organisation; without which chaos and anarchy might result. In a predictable, stable environment such management tasks are really all that are required, and hence for many years the term 'clinical management' has been used to describe the participation of professionals in such activities. However, when there is a need for change, perhaps a difficult and potentially unpopular change, then it is leaders who challenge, motivate and inspire others towards the new vision who become critical. It is in the continual change and upheaval experienced by the NHS in recent decades that we see the explanation of the refocusing on leadership from management, and the increasingly important role of doctors as leaders.

However, it is important to recognise that delivering and maintaining change, possibly initiated by leaders, almost certainly requires management expertise. *The two functions are really complementary, varying in emphasis and being more or less appropriate at different times depending on circumstances.*

It is possible to have too much or too little of either management or leadership. Kotter writes that 'Strong management with no leadership tends to entrench an organization in deadly bureaucracy. Strong leadership with no management risks chaos.' The organisation itself may be threatened as a result.

## Implications for a newly qualified GP

There are two particular aspects that follow from the previous discussion.

- The first relates to the nature of the task being undertaken and whether it emphasises more or less the skills of management or leadership. This therefore focuses on the type of activity and how it might be analysed.
- It follows that, once the task is understood, the individuals involved need to be assessed to see if they have the necessary skills and that these skills are similar or complementary in different individuals. For example, in the scenario, which individuals have the ability to show leadership in a time of change? And which are better at managing the processes aligned more to a period of stability?

In terms of the task element we could take a checklist such as that offered by Gardner,[6] who divides management and leadership into two distinct sets of skills or orientations. If we apply some of these statements to the scenario presented at the beginning of this chapter we can see that certain elements lend themselves to a much more managerial focus than leadership.

For example, working through the exact procedures and arrangements that will be involved in commissioning, how the contracts will be set and whether similar systems already exist in the potential partner practice are critical *managerial* tasks. They will need a focus on detail and an understanding of current systems.

In contrast the whole issue of what the practice's approach to commissioning should be, considering a partnership with others and bringing all of the practice team to the same place in understanding, will require a vision of what it would look like, positive communication of the advantages, and influence upon those who are resistant. In other words it will require leadership. This will be absolutely key and we need therefore to understand more about leadership and how it might be enacted in the practice setting.

Table 10.1 ○ ***Management and leadership***

| Management focus | Leadership focus |
|---|---|
| 1 • Focus on impact in current situation | 1 • Long-term, visionary, futuristic |
| 2 • Constrained by the task in hand | 2 • 'Outside the box', bigger picture |
| 3 • Limited to own work area | 3 • Influence others outside their own group. Go beyond bureaucratic boundaries |
| 4 • Expectation that the defined task will be completed | 4 • Emphasise motivation, values |
| 5 • Work within set of parameters | 5 • Politically astute, cope with differing expectations from a range of stakeholders |
| 6 • Meet expectations | 6 • Think in terms of change and renewal |

*Source*: after Gardner.[6]



### Clinical leadership in general practice

There is increasing support for the view that without the engagement of clinicians many of the reforms and improvements sought in health care cannot be delivered.[7] The challenge in general practice might be considerable. Jakeman,[8] a GP himself, reports that the term 'clinical leadership' is not familiar in general practice and was not to be found in a search of the index of the *British Journal of General Practice*. He asserts that this is not necessarily because of the absence of the necessary skills but more to do with the history of general practice, with its individualistic patient focus, personal autonomy (and often isolation) and a weaker sense of GPs' role in the health economy and collective framework. Interestingly he also notes that commissioning as a process might require a transformational leadership style to influence colleagues to the concept and a more transactional (managerial) focus to deal with the contractual issues.

What then do we know about leadership and how will the GP recognise his or her qualities or style in providing the necessary leadership? Despite many years of research and considerable resource allocation there is little consensus about leadership. Many definitions exist but in essence it would seem to be a process of influence towards a particular goal, outcome or idea. It might reside within an individual towards others, or perhaps be more collective within a team and so have aspects of reciprocal 'influence' and 'followership'.

---

## What is a leader?

The initial approach to understanding leadership focused upon traits or characteristics possessed, perhaps uniquely, by leaders. Very long lists of characteristics emerged but with little consensus, and these characteristics were certainly not possessed exclusively by leaders. Traditionally the model is essentially that of a heroic leader who rises to a challenge. This approach has not established an agreed list of behaviours or competences, rather relying on descriptors and perceptions of those heading organisations or processes. This positional view of leadership can seem less relevant to the complex environment of today, where a range of skills and problem-solving ability is needed at different times, by a wider range of individuals.

Examining the lists of words associated with leadership is typically not terribly enlightening for the aspiring leader. You will almost certainly feel that you possess some, but how many are needed, to what degree and in what combination? Since individuals do emerge as leaders with an almost infinite set of combinations of personal characteristics then one can conclude that:

- there are lots of ways in which people can lead
- no universal prescribed set of characteristics is required
- all individuals are capable of making a contribution as leaders in different ways.

Subsequent approaches to leadership turned more to an assessment of 'situational factors', i.e. what was it in the situation that determined the type of leadership required and therefore who might emerge as leader.

This recognition that a person could change the leadership style, depending on the circumstances, led to the most recent construction of leadership, that of *shared or distributed leadership*. This model rejects the notion of a single, superior leader operating in a top-down style directing others. Instead it recognises the complexity of today, the emphasis upon teamwork and the distribution of qualities across a number of staff who, better educated than previously, can all contribute as leaders in a more collective way.

## Application to general practice

Rushmer *et al.*[9] discussing leadership and empowerment in relation to the learning organisation provide a helpful example of leadership in action, in the context of general practice. Modern leadership might be enacted in general practice by 'leaders' engaging in the following types of behaviours:

1 ▷ asking new and challenging questions to probe new or existing beliefs and assumptions, in order to identify new ways of working. For instance, to look at multidisciplinary working rather than traditional uni-disciplinary approaches

2 ▷ having the expertise to be able to see possibilities and to conceptualise the future when others might see confusion

3 ▷ communicating well, starting with listening, and engaging with all relevant members of a team

4 ▷ facilitating understanding of any change required and modelling the values underlying the direction

5 ▷ driving forward changes when necessary but having the emotional awareness to be able to support and encourage others when needed.



Figure 10.1 ○ ***Domains and competences***

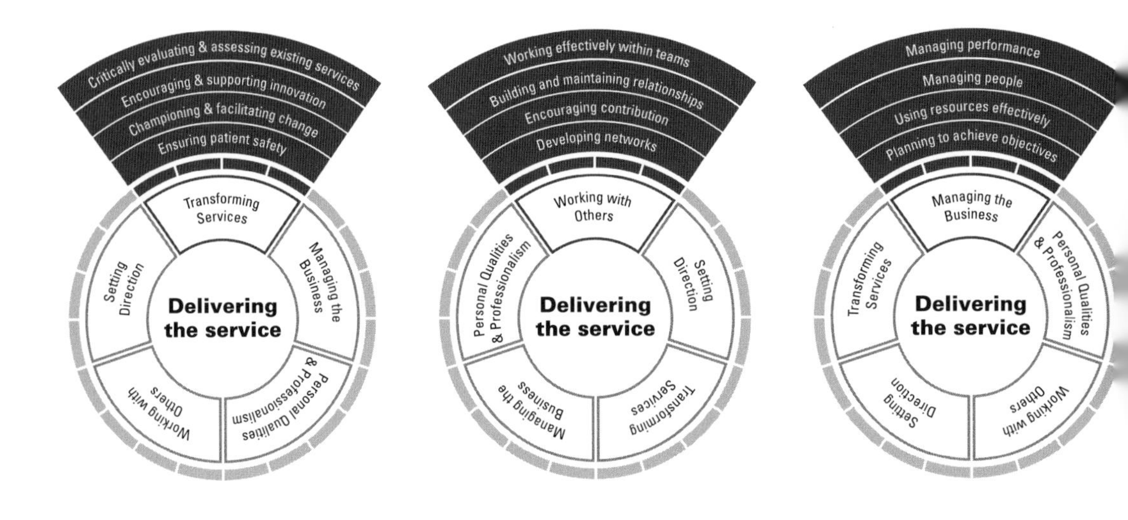

The challenge for effective management and leadership in general practice must be to recognise the value and strength of good management of current systems, but to go beyond this to develop a vision of the future that can be shared by the team. This is not the responsibility of one person but a collective task that effective leadership can support and promote. So for our new partner leading the commissioning, he or she now knows that it is not his or her job to lead alone, and that many members of the team will need to show leadership. Each learner's style will vary according to the task, the context and also the personal characteristics of the individual. Some of the tasks might need to be carried out by an individual who has a strongly managerial style, while some will need to be done by an individual who will show vision and point the way forwards.

## Leadership development in the future: the Medical Leadership Competency Framework

In 2008 the Medical Leadership Competency Framework was published. It exists as five domains in which all doctors should be able to show that they are competent. The project was undertaken jointly by the Academy of Royal Medical Colleges and the NHS Institute for Innovation and Improve-

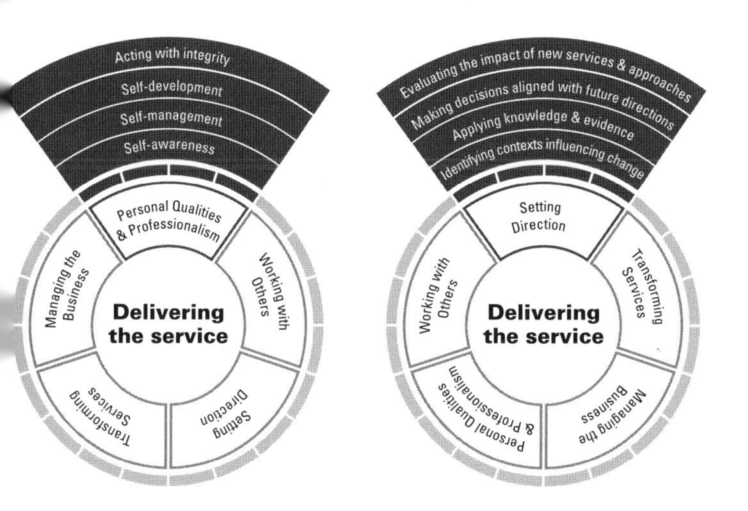


*Source*: NHS Institute for Innovation and Improvement: www.institute.nhs.uk/assessment_tool/general/leadership_and_doctors.html. Crown copyright material is reproduced with the permission of the Controller of OPSI.

ment in 2006. The framework was developed after a review of the academic literature and after extensive consultation with undergraduate and postgraduate deans, medical students, doctors in training, tutors and course organisers, educational experts, the British Medical Association (BMA) and the General Medical Council (GMC). At the time of writing work is being carried out to insert the competency framework into all the postgraduate medical curricula through PMETB (Postgraduate Medical Education and Training Board), and undergraduate curricula through the GMC document *Tomorrow's Doctors*. The aim is for all doctors to look at their leadership skills, from the start of medical school and throughout their career, integrating their personal development with the acquisition of clinical and management skills.

The goal of the framework is that all doctors should be able to lead, within a healthcare structure that requires shared leadership. It aims for doctors to have insight into their strengths and weaknesses in this area, to enable good clinical practice, enhance patient safety and ensure a safe workplace.



Figure 10.1 on the previous page illustrates the five domains and competences needed by doctors.

## Questions

1 ▷ Why might we describe the primary care context as increasingly complex?

2 ▷ Why does this complexity lead to a greater focus on leadership over management?

3 ▷ Is the distinction between management and leadership clear?

4 ▷ Why do some people characterise management as 'bad' and leadership as 'good'?

5 ▷ An organisation full of individuals playing leadership roles might become chaotic – why?

6 ▷ What is it about tasks that suggest they need more of a management than leadership focus?

7 ▷ Why is it helpful to distinguish between management and leadership when considering the task to be done?

8 ▷ Is service improvement in the NHS possible without engaging clinicians?

**9** ▷ Why might clinical leadership be relatively new to general practice?

**10** ▷ Why might commissioning as a process need a contribution of transactional and transformational leadership?

**11** ▷ How might distributed leadership help tackle complex problems?

**12** ▷ What are some of the key tasks for effective leaders in a general practice setting?

**References**

1 • Chapman JA. The work of leaders in new organisational contexts *Journal of Management Development* 2001; **20(1)**: 55–68.

2 • Plesk PE, Greenhalgh T. The challenge of complexity in healthcare *British Medical Journal* 2001; **323**: 625–8.

3 • Grint S. Management or leadership *Journal of Health Service Research Policy* 2002; **7(4)**: 248–51.

4 • Spurgeon P, Cragg R. Is it management or leadership? In: R Chambers, K Mohanna, D Wall, *et al.* (eds). *Leadership for General Practice* Oxford: Radcliffe Press, 2007.

5 • Kotter JP. *What Leaders Really Do* Boston: Harvard Business Review Press, 1999.

6 • Gardner J. *On Leadership* New York: The Free Press, 1990.

7 • Ham C. Improving the performance of health services: the role of clinical leadership *Lancet* 2003; **361**: 1978–80.

8 • Jakeman P. Clinical leadership in general practice *Clinician in Management* 2004; **12**: 117–22.

9 • Rushmer R, Kelly D, Lough M, *et al.* Introducing the learning practice – III: leadership, empowerment, protected time and reflective practice as core contextual conditions *Journal of Evaluation in Clinical Practice* 2004; **10**: 399–405.

# Time management

# 11

*Robert Cragg*

### *Scenario*

*You work in a small-town practice. The practice comprises two senior partners, a GP registrar and yourself, a recently appointed salaried GP. You arrive at work on the first Tuesday after the Easter break to find one of the partners looking anxious. It appears that the GP registrar has been delayed returning from holiday and the locum who has been covering the other partner's sick leave has failed to turn up, with the agency unable to offer alternative cover.*

*You and the senior partner have eight surgeries to do, 50 results to go through and at least seven home visits to perform. There is simply too much work for the two of you to perform. Furthermore you are celebrating you parents' ruby wedding anniversary in a local restaurant at 7.30 this evening, so working late is not an option.*

*You have two receptionists, a practice nurse (with her own list) and contact details for the district nursing team at your disposal.*

*Your senior partner is preparing for a key meeting with the PCT and so it is left to you to lead the practice through this scenario. You attended a half-day training course on time management during your Vocational Training Scheme (VTS) training programme last year. How can you use the knowledge you assimilated to get you successfully through the working day?*



## Introduction

> *Don't say you don't have enough time. You have exactly the same number of hours per day that were given to Helen Keller, Pasteur, Michelangelo, Mother Teresa, Leonardo da Vinci, Thomas Jefferson, and Albert Einstein.*
>
> (*H. Jackson Brown*)[1]

In the NHS practitioners face a plethora of conflicting challenges balancing the quality of care against the quantity of patients, prioritising between elective and emergency caseloads, juggling our administration and medical responsibilities. Staff shortages, inefficient colleagues and interruptions can further compound our workloads.

These workload demands are not periodic or predictable, but are dynamic and constantly changing. Despite the demands placed on practitioners our services relentlessly insist that clinical and managerial decisions are made in a timely manner. In order to work within this taxing environment all professionals need to develop their own coping strategies to equip them to competently manage their time effectively.[2] We need to make and revise decisions about how we use our time, to best serve our patients.

Time management is a discipline comprising tools and techniques that, once introduced into your working life, can enable you to be more productive at work, whilst enabling you to maximise your free time. As with any discipline, time management requires focus and initially requires both effort and concentration to overcome old habits and attitudes, engraining new, more effective working practices.[2]

This chapter will provide some of the knowledge of practical skills to develop a personal approach to time management, as well as providing tips on how to improve the time effectiveness of others.



## Benefits of time management

Edward Young wrote 'Procrastination is the thief of time.'[3]

The benefits of time management are self-evident. Being in control of time enables a clear focus to be retained on objectives, the knock-on of which leads to increased productivity. Prioritising workloads in the absence of external pressures is more likely to lead to correct decision-making about how time is managed. Working in a time-limited manner can lead to panic and susceptibility to interruptions, allowing others to dictate the working day.[2]

*Social pursuits should not be compromised by having to stay late due to personal inefficiency. The ruby wedding meal would be a crime to miss and reflects the commitments many of us have to family and recreation out of hours.*

## Identifying what needs to be done

The irony of time management strategies is they take time to perform – it is necessary to invest time, to save time. The exceptional circumstances of the scenario demand that forethought is given as to how the working day should be tackled. A good habit to get into is taking a quiet ten minutes, at the start of a working day, to think through what needs to be achieved. An age-old time management mantra is 'STOP', standing for:

*Stop, Think, Operationalise, Perform.*

During this time it helps to devise a realistic 'to-do list'. Recording activities in this way focuses attention on the job in hand and ensures that key jobs are not forgotten. During a 'normal working day' your to-do list might include important administrative tasks, home visits and the surgery format of the day, but might also include a note to make time to speak to the district nurses or phone a colleague.

A typical GP 'to-do-list' should focus on the aims of the day, namely to get patients seen both in the practice and in the community whilst acting on abnormal results. Allocating a time to each task enables you to keep a check on progress as you proceed through your working day. In this way all our activities should be mapped as efficiently as computerised appointment schedules.

When considering the abnormal scenario mentioned at the start of the chapter the following list might have been drawn up (in no particular order of priority).

**1** ▷ Call the locum agency to see if support is available tomorrow or if help can be provided this afternoon.

**2** ▷ Talk to the practice manager about your superannuation refund that has not been paid.

**3** ▷ Reduce demand by triaging patients on the phone to see if they still need their appointment and identifying if any patients would be willing to attend surgery tomorrow, instead of today.

**4** ▷ Start your surgery on time.

**5** ▷ Signing routine referral letters from yesterday's surgery.

**6** ▷ Contact the district nurse team to see if the home patients known to them can be triaged by the community nursing team and have their visit delayed.

**7** ▷ Go through the mounting pile of non-patient-related post and circulars.

**8** ▷ Get the administration team to look for exceptional asterisked results that require action, filing all routines and bringing urgencies to your attention.

**9** ▷ Determine if the practice nurse has any capacity to see specific patients in addition to her existing list.

**10** ▷ Complete PMAs and insurance forms.

## Prioritising what needs to be done

The way in which to-do lists are prioritised is critical to making the most of a working day. Covey helped develop the theory of prioritisation, maintaining the belief that all tasks can be analysed over the axes of importance and urgency. Each activity therefore has a value of importance and urgency unique to that task, which Covey believes can be mapped out onto a two-by-two matrix. Each person's perspective of urgency and importance will differ, as all individuals are unique in the way that issues are prioritised based on individual value base or working preference.[4]

Figure 11.1 prioritises the previous to-do list.



Figure 11.1 ○ ***Prioritisation along axes of urgency and importance***

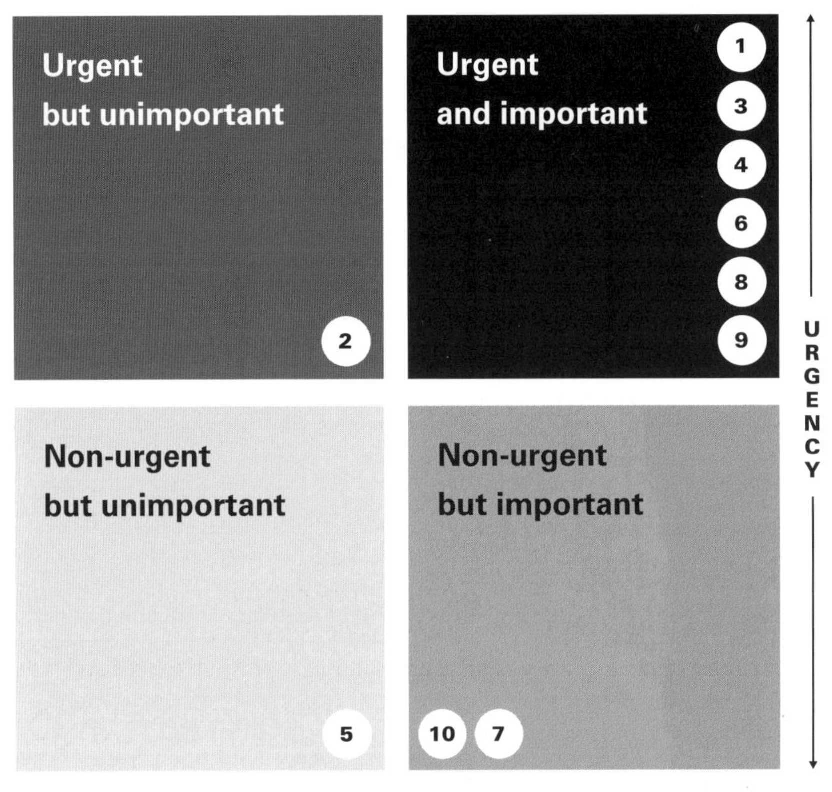

Broadly speaking, urgency is usually defined or dictated by the needs of others, e.g. acute patients' need or organisational deadlines, whereas importance relates to more developmental activities. Covey believes that we ensure we perform working tasks that are 'not urgent but important' where we have the time and concentration to do a job well. This is difficult to achieve in the NHS but underlies the preventive side of medicine, which underlies much of modern-day general practice.[4] When delegated a task from others it is vital to assess workload before accepting the task – only taking on more work if it is possible given other commitments. This balance is particularly difficult for doctors in training who must balance appearing approachable without being a 'pushover', juggling the needs of the service against individual training needs.

---

## Delegation



Once tasks have been prioritised decisions on which tasks can be delegated and to whom must be made. Good delegation can reap many rewards for the incumbents of this skill, saving valuable time to invest both in their own development and advancement.

Delegating tasks to peers and junior staff enables individuals to assist in the development of other people and groom successors. If applied correctly, delegating tasks to others can be motivational. Conversely poor delegation baffles, aggravates, induces stress and leads to potential failure of achieving the task.

Delegation is not just simple instruction or telling someone else what to do; delegation of tasks must be done in such a way that the person given the task feels empowered or receives an incentive, be it developmental or bestowing responsibility or challenge.[2]

People often mistake delegation as an *'all or nothing'* process, with the individual delegated the task having to assume full responsibility for the task in question. This approach to delegation can be too restrictive, narrowing the range of individuals upon which the dealer can call upon. A more effective way is to visualise delegation as a scale of accumulative responsibility that can be conferred upon the individual being delegated to.

The critical step is to ensure the *freedom allocated within the task matches the competence and reliability of the person being delegated to*. In this way the relationship, confidence and trust develops between team members, allowing the range and skill of the tasks allotted to increase.

Like setting objectives delegated tasks must follow key guidelines:

- ▷ setting explicit jobs under mutual consent
- ▷ these 'jobs' are quantifiable, pragmatic, time-specific, moral and documented.

Delegation applied in this manner goes hand in hand with the methods of training.

**In the case of our scenario, the newly appointed GP will have to use all of his or her prior experience of practice staff in the allocation of the following tasks:**

- ▶ telephone triage of appointments made for later today to see if the appointment is appropriate for the patient to postpone
- ▶ looking forward at the rest of the week's appointment to free up spaces
- ▶ identifying experienced clinical staff in the practice to share the burden of some of the urgents
- ▶ appointing an individual to identify abnormal results to bring to the attention of a GP
- ▶ identify members of the wider team to see if they are able to assist with any of the home visits, or checking if some visits can be done at another time.

**The allocation of these tasks needs careful consideration, matching the competence and responsibility level of team members.**



## Why do people fail to delegate?

Doctors reported with performance issues often have problems delegating tasks to others.[5] The reasons underlying such difficulties are varied but might include:

- ▷ desire for perfectionism
- ▷ doubting the ability of peers
- ▷ failure to relinquish control
- ▷ failure to develop trust or take the time to invest in peer relations sufficient to ask for help and support
- ▷ poor communication.

These problems commonly occur in transition stages in career progression because, as doctors gain extra responsibility and autonomy, they can be reluctant to let go of the more routine and basic procedures they used to enjoy performing, or reluctant to take on the responsibility for directing junior staff.

## Poor time management leads to productivity issues

Poor time management can lead to a series of efficiency issues.

### *Lapse administration*

Not taking the time to manage you personal administration leads to disorganisation. Hoarding needless administration, poor filing and untidiness leads to loss or delay in finding, compiling and sending key correspondence. Writing clinical correspondences and referrals the size of *War and Peace* is unnecessary.

### *Taking on too much*

Synonymous with individuals who fail to delegate is the issue of burnout. It can be difficult to say 'no' or to 'ask for help' but there are occasions when all of us need to call on others.



### *Not making time to save time*

Organisational problems in the day-to-day running of surgeries or administrative systems will persist unless time is taken to sit down and address them. In today's target-driven service it can be difficult to take time out from the ever-increasing pressure of patient and service demand, to discuss developments and improvement ideas. However, taking a half-day once in a while can soon pay dividends through enhanced efficiency in the medium- to long-term. The document *Going Lean in the NHS* provides a short commentary explaining how clinical groups can rethink clinical services to improve productivity and time efficiency, reduce waste and lower NHS costs.[6]

### *Turning a blind eye*

Productivity issues residing in an individual can thus impact on the wider team.

System failings can be allowed to persist if time is not taken to correct poor performance capability in our teams. Team members who fail to resolve productivity issues in their peers become ineffective at their own jobs, as they try to compensate for colleagues' incompetence for the good of their team. Therefore it falls on the responsibility of peers and managers alike to address performance issues. Historically, addressing inadequacies in colleagues has been erratic within the medical profession; however, the culture is gradually changing, with appraisal becoming the norm, as the NHS nears revalidation and recertification of doctors at every level of service.

## Time wasting

*For tyme y-lost may not recovered be.*

(*Geoffrey Chaucer* [*c. 1340–1400*])[7]

There are days in any careers in which drive and motivation are lost and when procrastination can take hold.[8] Such dawdling is normal on an occasional basis but if not controlled can all too soon edge its way into daily practice, bad habits take hold and concentration lapses more and more frequently. A few top tips to keep on track include: don't delay surgery start time through idle chatter – the time can be difficult to make up once surgery has started:



- avoid getting embroiled with practice politics if there are other people better placed to intervene
- if you can't fit everything into your day, make time to discuss it with your colleagues and managers, to look at solutions early before problems develop
- avoid unnecessary interruptions and perhaps allow all urgent calls to a nominated duty doctor, who has time allocated to deal with them
- where possible work on an 'empty' desk principle. Keep up to date with referrals and paperwork, and avoid leaving an ever-increasing in-tray; something important at the bottom might never be reached
- make good use of tea breaks; breaks to refresh the mind and concentration are essential.

## Delay can be positive

Occasionally delaying action can be the correct thing to do.[2] The prime example of this trend is observed when an individual is tired; it might be wise not to tackle jobs that require tact and sensitivity, ideally saving such actions for when there is space to do this properly, when the individual concerned is rejuvenated.

Some aspects of modern communications can help, as well as hinder time management. Emails and electronic task lists can be put aside until there is a suitable time to do them properly. It is all too easy to become addicted to electronic communications, attaching immediacy to and unnecessarily prioritising the content of emails, which often do not warrant an instant reply.

Temporary delays in a crisis can give time for new information on solutions to come to light or allow better delegation. For instance it might be appropriate to delay putting in an advert for a new member of staff until those involved have fully decided on the most appropriate job specification, but inappropriate to delay visiting a patient in need. The urgency of the situation needs to be thought through to prevent patient care being harmed.

## Conclusion

Time management is a discipline upon which the skills of delegation and prioritisation are essential. The extreme scenario highlighted in this chapter is one that we all could face.

Worthwhile free time and going home at a good time for a quality, stress-free evening is key to maintaining a healthy work–life balance. This is only possible if we remain disciplined during office hours – resolute to our objectives. Being in command of time makes you a safer clinician and a trustworthy colleague to work with, as others perceive you as effective and responsive.

## Questions

1 ▷ What are the benefits of effective time management?

2 ▷ How can you avoid wasting time in your current daily activities?

3 ▷ According to Covey what are the two axes of prioritisation?

4 ▷ What strategies can you use to prioritise your daily workload?

5 ▷ What conflicts on our time do we face in today's NHS?

6 ▷ How can you delegate effectively?

7 ▷ Why do people fail to delegate?

8 ▷ What performance issues are synonymous with poor time management?

**References**

1 • Jackson Brown H. *Life's Little Instruction Book* Nashville, TN: Thomas Nelson, 1991.

2 • Maitland I. *Managing Your Time* (Management Shaper series) London: Chartered Institute of Personnel and Development, 1995.

3 • Young E. *The Complaint, and the Consolation; or, Night Thoughts* New York: Dover Publications, 1996.

4 • Covey S. *First Things First* New York: Simon & Schuster, 1999.

5 • Sutherland V, Cooper C L. *De-stressing Doctors: a self-management guide* Oxford: Butterworth-Heinemann, 2002.

6 • NHS Institute for Innovation and Improvement. *Going Lean in the NHS* Coventry: NHS Institute for Innovation and Improvement, 2007.

7 • Chaucer G. *Troilus and Criseyde* Harmondsworth: Penguin, 1971.

8 • McGee-Cooper A. *Time Management for Unmanageable People* New York: Bantam Doubleday Dell, 1994.

# Motivating the individual

# 12

*Jag Dhaliwal*

---

### Scenario

*It's been six months since you joined your new practice and you've now had an opportunity to get to know the members of the team. You have found it a pleasant place to work and the team as a whole appears highly motivated and contented.*

*The puzzle is your nurse practitioner, Alex.*

*Alex is acknowledged to be a 'bright cookie'. She obtained a bachelor's degree in nursing with distinction and has attended umpteen courses to develop her advanced practice. However, she only ever seems to do the absolute minimum required to get by and her lack of motivation now appears to be having a negative effect on the rest of the nursing team.*

*What can you do to re-energise and motivate Alex?*

---

## Introduction

Building and sustaining a successful practice depends upon building and sustaining motivation amongst your practice colleagues.

To do this, a GP will need to:

- ▷ motivate and develop the various subgroups and teams that make up your practice (see Chapters 5 and 13)
- ▷ motivate each individual within your practice (the subject of this chapter).

The chapter will begin with an exploration of two influential theories of motivation, and will then look at a structured approach to analysing and addressing the above scenario – an approach that doctors will find reassuringly familiar!

## What is meant by 'motivation'?

The word 'motivation' is often used ambiguously.[1] For instance, what does it mean 'to motivate' someone and, indeed, is it possible to do so? What is the difference between someone who does a job 'for the love of it' and someone who 'is in it for the money'? Indeed, does it really matter as long as the result is the same?

This is where some of the ideas and models about motivation can help to understand the meaning of 'motivation', and can help to understand how to motivate an employee or work colleague as mentioned in the scenario above.

When looking at groups, Maslow's hierarchy model is helpful since it is logical to conclude that if the physiological needs of individuals are not being met they are unlikely to care about higher-order motivators such as 'status' or 'self-actualisation'.[2]

For example, contrast the following:



*There's not enough income coming in each month to pay the mortgage. Any work will do – I'll work hard to stop the house being repossessed (Physiological Tier)*

*versus*

*It's great having the nice house, the car and the foreign holidays. But it's boring doing blood pressure readings all morning! Shouldn't there be* more *to life? Perhaps it's time for a career change... (Self-Actualisation Tier).*

Individuals might organise their priorities in a way that doesn't always fit within Maslow's hierarchy. For example:

*It's a tough role: The hours are long, I get very little free time and I know the pay is better in other parts of the country. But I love this job because I've always wanted to do this. I wouldn't change this job in a million years.*

As discussed in Chapter 13 on change management, when we are considering an individual, an assortment of different motivators will be involved. Examples might include 'pay', 'job security', 'personal security', 'opportunities for career advancement', 'length of holidays', 'cover for sickness absence', 'hours of work', 'opportunities for pursuing outside work', 'relationship with colleagues' and so on.

### *How can you seek to tailor your approach so that each individual member of your team is 'motivated'?*

To understand the concept of motivation further, it is useful to explore two influential models: Herzberg's theory of motivation and expectancy theory.

### *Herzberg's theory of motivation*

Herzberg (building upon the work of various psychologists and sociologists) clarified the difference between 'being motivated by the work itself' (sometimes termed 'intrinsic motivation') and 'doing a job because of the positive or negative rewards that result' (sometimes termed 'extrinsic motivation').[3]

Further, Herzberg explored the relationship between 'job satisfaction' (and hence motivation) and 'dissatisfaction': Contrary to what you might expect, 'satisfaction' is not the opposite of 'dissatisfaction' when we are considering motivation.

### *'Satisfaction' and 'dissatisfaction' are not opposites*

Based upon research he conducted amongst employees in a wide variety of organisations (followed by research conducted in different countries), Herzberg found that the factors leading to 'satisfaction' are *different* from those factors that cause 'dissatisfaction'.

Table 12.1 helps to illustrate this.

Table 12.1 ○ ***Factors related to satisfaction and dissatisfaction***

| **Factors related to satisfaction (intrinsic motivation)** | **Factors related to dissatisfaction** |
|---|---|
| Achievement | Company policy |
| Recognition | Supervision |
| Work itself | Relationship with employer |
| Responsibility | Work conditions |
| Advancement | Salary |
| Growth | Personal life |
| | Status |
| | Security |

*Source*: adapted from Herzberg.[3]

So, for example, lack of clear, equitable company policies might be expected to lead to *dissatisfaction*. ('Why can he or she always get holiday leave during August when my request is always declined?')

But introducing such policies would be unlikely to result in high levels of *satisfaction* and ignite the practice team's motivation to steam into work on a Monday morning! ('I can't wait to get in and experience the delight of our Annual Leave Policy!')

Rather, by introducing fair, transparent policies, the best that can be hoped for is *reduced dissatisfaction*. Similarly, a lack of security might lead to individuals being dissatisfied with their place of work, but installing Fort Knox-style protection would be unlikely to result in higher levels of satisfaction and enthusiasm!

Conversely, it's possible to be highly motivated to do a particular job (perhaps because it allows possibilities for personal growth) but at the same time feel dissatisfied with it.

Think about the difference between:

*someone working at* Justajob Practice, *which offers a good package of pay, reasonable working hours and job security – but little possibility for career development. The individual is satisfied (with the conditions) but not motivated*

compared with

*Someone who is motivated but dissatisfied working at* Freneticdays Practice, *where working hours are long and practice profits are less than the national average – but patient appreciation levels are high and the practice offers clinically challenging work and opportunities for developing a special interest.*



### *Motivators and 'hygiene factors'*

The above example illustrates Herzberg's thinking about motivation.

There is a difference between being:

*intrinsically motivated by a job*

versus

*doing a job because of the extrinsic benefits it produces and/or doing a job to avoid negative consequences.*

As such, motivators that produce *intrinsic* motivation relate to the nature of the job itself. If the job itself is felt to be interesting and allows scope for growth, advancement and achievement, it is likely to enthuse employees.

This is different from doing a job either because it offers benefits for compliance or punishments for non-compliance – which Herzberg terms 'hygiene factors' or in everyday parlance 'carrots' and 'sticks'.

A 'stick' would be the threat of disciplinary action if you persistently fail to turn up at work on a Monday morning, for example. The possibility of the 'stick' of a negative outcome 'propels' an individual (from behind) to turn up to work on time.

A 'carrot' might be an enhanced rate of pay for agreeing to work at the weekend or a 'pat on the back' from your employer. This 'propels' the individual forward towards the positive inducement being offered.

This difference between 'motivators' and 'carrots and sticks' *is* important because carrots and sticks cause movement. By putting in place negative or positive propelling factors you can get individuals to 'move' and do what you want them to do.

#### *But the reward or punishment needs to be repeated to get further movement*

For example, following a pay rise, the productivity of most employees rises, for a time, but performance eventually always plateaus. Why is this? It is thought that as individuals get used to the higher rate of pay (and their expenditure rises to swallow up the extra earnings), this becomes 'the norm' and 'expected'. It would take another pay rise to produce further increases in productivity. So, when considering the scenario, offering Alex a 20 per cent pay increase might well get her 'motivated' to do more work in the short term. In the long term, if she is not motivated by the job itself, the evidence suggests that her performance will eventually return to the baseline before the pay increase.

*Motivators*, therefore, are best related to the nature of the job itself. In this sense, someone who is 'motivated' can be seen as having his or her own 'internal combustion engine of energy' and will want to do his or her job well, independently of any external carrots or sticks. Herzberg's recommendation is to design jobs so that they are 'enriched' with intrinsic motivating factors (see Table 12.1).

Relating Herzberg's ideas back to Alex, therefore, it is possible to see that there are two aspects to consider.

▷ Is Alex dissatisfied with her job?
▷ Is Alex no longer motivated by her job?

How might her job be *enriched*, so that it *would* motivate her?

▷ What 'carrots and sticks' might be put into place to get her to comply with the responsibilities laid out in her contract of employment?

Notice that 'motivators' and 'carrots and sticks' are not alternatives or 'either/or' options: both sets of factors need to be present in order to obtain the highest level of performance from individuals working in our practices.

- ▷ When considering 'carrots and sticks' we are looking at the related area of performance management (which is considered in Chapter 4).
- ▷ Our focus in this chapter is on motivating factors.

## Expectancy theory

Expectancy theory[4,5] considers the calculation (which might be conscious or subconscious) that each of us make when weighing up whether to put effort into achieving a goal – or not.

Figure 12.1 illustrates this theory:



Figure 12.1 ○ ***The Lawler–Porter diagram of expectancy theory***

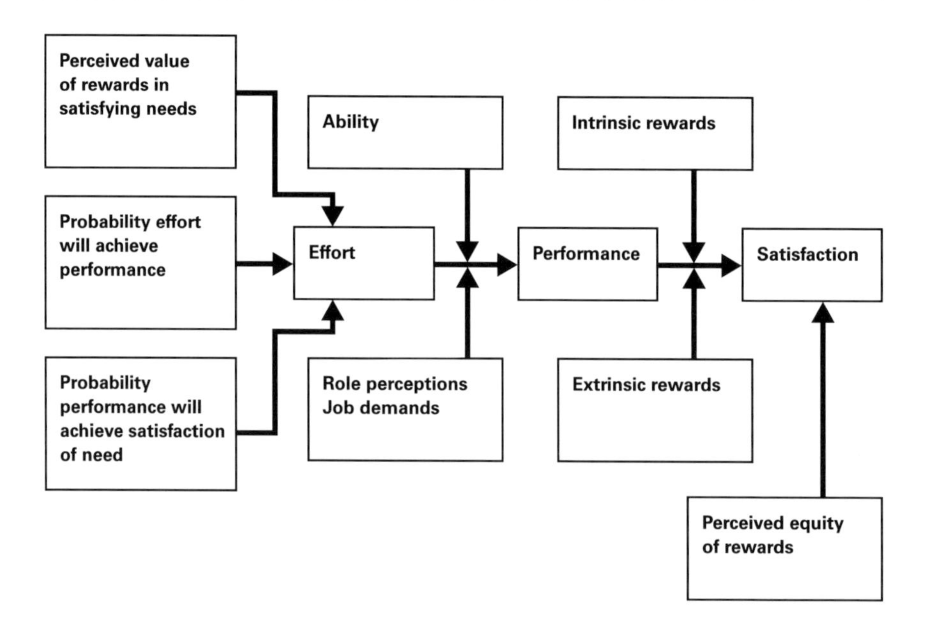


Prior to putting effort into an activity, the model states that individuals weigh up their own needs (i.e. thus incorporating the idea of Maslow's hierarchy of needs) and the *perceived* likelihood that the outcome of the effort will satisfy those needs. Taking an example from Charles Dickens:

> *If the Artful Dodger perceives education as offering little opportunity to escape life on the streets, he is unlikely to put much effort into his schoolwork.*

Not all effort produces performance. Much as any aspiring schoolchild might try, it's highly improbable that each and every performance in football will match David Beckham's – leading to the inevitable personal calculation that pursuing a goal as a professional footballer is 'not worth the effort'. In other circumstances, that same schoolchild might be able to achieve a good performance, but realise that this stellar performance will not satisfy his or her future needs. If earning income is important, spending hours training to win the egg-and-spoon race is not a good use of effort because it won't result in increased income.

In translating effort into performance, one's ability is clearly important. Natural ability combines with acquired ability, and this is where education and training come into play through helping to boost our innate competencies. There might be factors that interfere in translating effort into performance, such as other job demands. Importantly, if a nurse's perception of his or her role differs from the perception held by the GP employers, the nurse might fail to achieve his or her goal because of the mismatch in expectations.



Finally, any degree of satisfaction will be influenced by the *perception* of the equity of the rewards on offer: an individual might be very happy to work hard making widgets to earn £10 an hour ... that is until the morning it is learnt that, in the factory across town, workers are earning £20 an hour for the same job.

*Expectancy theory* is useful because it allows us to consider the interrelationship between the *expectation* of effort resulting in rewards and the *perception* of the value of those rewards.

Hence, in the case of Alex, further questions arise.

- ▷ What rewards does Alex hope to get from her job and how do these tie in to her wider needs?
- ▷ What does Alex perceive as her role and what does the practice expect of her?
- ▷ Does Alex perceive that she is being treated fairly?
- ▷ What package of measures might be needed to convince Alex that her effort in this role will translate into rewards that she desires?

Through seeking answers to these questions and combining these with answers to the questions that arose from our exploration of Herzberg's theory it is possible to build up a richer picture of 'what's going on with Alex'. By increasing understanding, there is a greater chance of success.

## The scenario

Charles Handy makes the analogy of the 'manager as general practitioner'.[1] According to Handy, the medical model of identifying symptoms, diagnosing the root cause of the symptoms, and deciding upon a management plan, having considered the available options, can and should be applied to management problems.

Indeed, he argues persuasively that many supposedly intractable management problems actually arise from a failure to follow the above schema methodically. An example is 'using the same plan' – whatever the cause of the problem and without considering the full range of actions that are possible. Examples of 'the same plan' in different scenarios might be 'We need an away day to boost morale' (without exploring why morale is low). Or 'The NHS needs restructuring to boost efficiency' (without analysing whether the root cause of NHS 'inefficiency' *is* its structure or other factors).



Using the medical model, therefore, we can explore the scenario in more detail.

### *Symptoms and obtaining a history*

It is known that Alex is well trained but it is stated that she does 'the absolute minimum required to get by'.

This needs further clarification.

In what way does Alex do 'the absolute minimum'? A list of concrete examples of what is meant by this statement is essential:

- ▷ first, it is important to be clear that there really is a problem *with Alex*. Could negative comments about Alex actually point to conflict within the practice and possibly even bullying of this member of staff? This is a different problem, therefore, from the 'lack of motivation' that was initially presented
- ▷ second, it is important to have clear examples of behaviour that demonstrate Alex's 'lack of motivation'. Such examples will be important, because it is only through contrasting her current behaviour with the practice's expectation that Alex can be given tangible goals for improvement, and ways of supporting her to achieve these goals might be discussed.

For example, it might be evident from the computer notes that Alex is not asking diabetic patients whether they are depressed or not, an important part of the depression parameter for the Quality and Outcomes Framework (QoF).

Or there might be aspects related to Alex's relationship with the practice team, e.g. Alex is *perceived* to be low in motivation because other members of the team find that she does not smile much and always rushes out of work at 5.30 p.m. 'on the dot' without saying goodbye.

The point is that if other members of the team are commenting on intangibles such as 'lack of energy', 'lack of motivation', etc., it is important to find out specifically what *observable behaviour* of Alex's is leading team members to draw these conclusions.

Should Alex's performance require disciplinary action in the future, such concrete examples will be essential to justifying any action. This is in much the same way that doctors take a complete history with the aim of helping patients but also with an auxiliary purpose of defending their actions, should a medico-legal challenge arise.

Once the above background history has been obtained, Alex's perspective needs to be explored (i.e. Alex's history needs to be taken).

The *way* in which this is done needs to be considered since a variety of options exist (these are discussed more fully in Chapter 7).



- ▷ Will Alex be approached formally at work or should she be engaged in conversation during an out-of-work event? Or how about just asking her if she wants to grab a coffee in the staffroom? What type of setting is appropriate at work – Alex's own consulting room? The practice manager's room? A GP partner's room?
- ▷ Who will approach Alex – the practice manager? A GP partner? The PCT nursing lead? Should it be someone with a close friendship with Alex or someone with a more formal relationship?

As a general rule of thumb, unless there is immediate concern, a more informal relaxed setting is preferable. This is because the goal is to get Alex to talk candidly about her role – her needs and expectations, motivators and negative factors causing dissatisfaction.

Understanding Herzberg's model and expectancy theory, we have already determined that we want to understand the following.

What does Alex need from her job? Is Alex dissatisfied with her job? i.e. does she feel dissatisfied because of problems with:

- ▷ company policy
- ▷ supervision
- ▷ relationship with employer
- ▷ work conditions
- ▷ salary
- ▷ personal life

- ▷ status
- ▷ security?

Is Alex not motivated by her job? i.e. does she feel that her job offers opportunities for:

- ▷ achievement
- ▷ recognition
- ▷ responsibility
- ▷ advancement
- ▷ growth
- ▷ enjoyment of the job itself?

How does Alex think her job might be modified or enriched so that it would motivate her? What does Alex perceive as her role and has the practice defined, in tangible, objective terms, what is expected of her? Does Alex perceive that she is being treated equitably compared with other members of the team? What package of measures might be needed to convince Alex that her effort in this role will translate into rewards that she desires?



Further, we need to consider what 'carrots and sticks' might be put into place to get Alex to comply with the responsibilities laid out in her contract of employment.

A GP's skills in clinical history-taking will be highly useful and transferable to this management situation, in helping you to obtain 'the history'.

Just as with clinical history-taking, the most successful approach is to actively listen to Alex's perspective and then proceed to open questions, allowing Alex to talk, followed later by more direct questions with the aim of obtaining all of the above information.

Equally, just as with clinical history-taking, where a doctor knows he or she 'needs to ask the patient about tenesmus' but will ask this in a way the patient understands, the above list suggests *what* information is needed: *how* this is asked depends upon re-phrasing the questions in more socially appropriate ways:

Examples of good questions are 'What do you like about working here?' 'Is being a nurse at this practice what you expected it to be?' 'What really excites you about your job?' 'What frustrates you in your role?' 'What would you like to do more of/what would you like to do less of in your role?'

### *Diagnosis*

Our list of possible diagnoses, therefore, for Alex's apparent 'lack of motivation' can be listed as:

- problems with the team – they are excluding Alex and their complaints do not seem to have an objective foundation
- problems with Alex
  - Alex only *appears* demotivated
    - aspects of her behaviour suggest to others that she is demotivated
    - Alex's perception of her role differs from that of other members of the practice: there is a mismatch between what Alex feels her role entails and what members of the practice feel her role entails
  - Alex *is* demotivated, due to
    - problems outside of work – at home, in her wider family, etc.
    - problems at work. She is dissatisfied with her job, i.e. a problem with
      - practice policy
      - supervision
      - relationship with employer
      - work conditions
      - salary
      - personal life
      - status
      - security
  - Alex is not motivated by her job because of a lack of opportunities for:
    - achievement
    - recognition
    - responsibility
    - advancement
    - growth
    - enjoyment of the job itself.



### Management plan

Needless to say, one or several of the 'diagnoses' listed above might result in the 'symptom' of Alex's perceived lack of motivation.

The two aspects towards addressing this issue will be:

- engaging in a dialogue with Alex and, where appropriate, the wider team, to see how the root causes might be addressed. This might simply mean a sharing of perspectives to achieve common understanding, or there might be an urgent need to take swift action (disciplinary action, in the case of harassment/bullying, for example). The goal is to reduce sources of dissatisfaction and ensure Alex's job is sufficiently challenging and rewarding to motivate her

- performance-managing Alex – the subject of Chapter 4. The key here is clarity. The practice needs to have a clear idea of what it expects of Alex; this needs to be communicated and understood, appropriate support must be offered, and an agreed mechanism to monitor and reward or sanction performance needs to be in place.

In conclusion, using theory around what motivates individuals and skills obtained as a doctor and a GP can help to diagnose and 'develop' team members and work colleagues. This can enable the whole practice to function at its best and ensure that patients are cared for by satisfied and motivated individuals.

## Questions



1. How does Maslow's hierarchy differ when considering individuals from groups?
2. What is meant by motivation?
3. What is the difference between intrinsic and extrinsic motivation?
4. How did Herzberg describe 'motivators'?
5. What does expectancy theory describe?
6. Why did Handy describe management as being akin to being a general practitioner?

### References

1 • Handy C. *Understanding Organizations* (fourth edn) Harmondsworth: Penguin, 1993.

2 • Maslow A. *Motivation and Personality* New York: Harper & Row, 1970.

3 • Herzberg F. One more time: how do you motivate employees? *Harvard Business Review* 1987; **65(5)**: 109–20.

4 • Vroom V. *Work and Motivation* New York: John Wiley, 1964.

5 • Porter L, Lawler E. *Managerial Attitudes and Performance* Homewood, IL: Dorsey Press, 1968.

# Change management

## Putting evidence into practice

# 13

*Veronica Wilkie*

### *Scenario*

*You are reviewing your patient feedback in a team meeting. None of the team is surprised to see the overwhelming response is for longer opening hours, as you are based in a satellite commuter town for a large city. You are also pleased to see that once your patients have an appointment they are very happy with the service you give. You have an idea that it would be possible for the practice to be open 8.00 a.m. to 8.00 p.m., with one of the five doctors each doing an early start and early finish (8.00 a.m. to 4.00 p.m.), a late start and late finish (11.00 a.m. to 8.00 p.m.), with the remaining three days being 'normal working days' (8.30 p.m. to 5.00 p.m.). Some extra cover for these is obviously required for annual study and sick leave. Your practice manager also wonders whether the staff could alter their working day to cover a wider opening time. You discuss this. One of your partners says it will happen 'over his dead body', another says 'It will only be the start. They'll have us working at night soon', and the office manager is concerned about changing staff contracts. You wonder whether there is any guidance on how to help individuals and organisations change.*

### Introduction

> *Change is inevitable in a progressive country. Change is constant.*
>
> (*Benjamin Disraeli* [1897])

Change is an imprecise science, and is certainly not new. Since the middle of the last century, the increasingly large and complex nature of organisations has led to increasing research and study of what makes individuals and groups of individuals change. The literature on change spans many disciplines, involving research in psychology, sociology, business and social policy, as well as in medical scientific papers, and ranges from purely descriptive reviews to in-depth analysis of change in particular situations. This chapter cannot provide all the answers but will attempt to give a broad outline of why an understanding of change management theory is useful.

The chapter will not give a review of all the theories available but will illustrate a few that a GP might find useful in practice.

---

## Evidence-Based Practice and the need to understand change management theory

At the start of the 1990s there was an increasing drive towards Evidence-Based Medicine (EBM), driven initially by now legendary writers on this subject David Sackett, Brian Haynes, Sharon Strauss and others. They have written widely and developed a series in the *Journal of the American Medical Association* (JAMA), looking at the way in which scientific findings are first chosen for their appropriateness for the clinical situation, then analysed systematically for scientific validity and then put into place. Each of the JAMA articles summarises a case and then discusses the research findings leading to the successful treatment options for the patient concerned.[1] The EBM movement grew, changed to Evidence-Based Health Care (recognising that it was not only practitioners of medicine that could benefit from its ways of practising) with a further change to Evidence-Based Practice (EBP) being suggested in 2003, recognising the benefits of the discipline to entire healthcare teams and their organisations.[2] The initial steps have been reformulated as:



**step 1** ▷ translation of uncertainly to an answerable question

**step 2** ▷ systemic retrieval of best evidence available

**step 3** ▷ critical appraisal of evidence for validity, clinical relevance and applicability

**step 4** ▷ application of results in practice

**step 5** ▷ evaluation of performance.

Whilst many books and hours of teaching are spent in looking at the first three steps, steps 4 and 5 are often ignored, or taught as if EBP was for individual change only. Change management theory is therefore an essential part of using the discipline of EBP within health care.

## Some evidence behind change management theory

### *Analysing the situation*

Evidence behind what makes individuals and organisations change has emerged over the last six decades. Some of what is relevant has been researched outside health care, as it looks at human behaviour in different contexts, and, unlike scientific research, earlier research is not necessarily superseded by later research. One of the most useful documents for looking at change is a review on *Managing Change* in the NHS by two healthcare researchers Valerie Iles and Kim Sutherland.[3] They make the following points:

- ▷ for all but the very simplest of changes the impact is multidimensional, and therefore the measures of effectiveness must capture all dimensions
- ▷ change programmes involve analysis of the precipitating event
- ▷ different people will analyse things differently.



Adding this to the complexity of finding relevant literature (and fulfilling step 2 of the five steps of EBP) makes change a difficult thing to study.

One of the earliest individuals to look at change was Lewin,[4] who thought of change in three stages. His initial work was as a physicist, but he subsequently expanded his philosophy by examining systems and organisations in the same light:

1. ▷ unfreezing the existing equilibrium (i.e. one where no change is needed)
2. ▷ creation of guilt or anxiety (and therefore an instability into the system allowing a movement towards change)
3. ▷ provision of psychological safety that converts anxiety into motivation to change.

Looking at the scenario at the start of the chapter, this could be translated into:

1. ▷ realising that longer opening hours are going to have to happen
2. ▷ becoming anxious about how to implement this without working longer hours, losing communication with colleagues or needing to spend more of a stretched practice budget
3. ▷ agreeing that change was needed and thinking 'outside the box' to new ways of working.

Lewin then developed his force field model proposing that there were driving forces and resisting forces to change, and that analysing each force could then make it easier to change the status quo. He suggested that it was better to reduce the resisting forces as increasing the driving forces might only lead to an increasing resistance.

Figure 13.1 ○ ***Lewin's force field model***

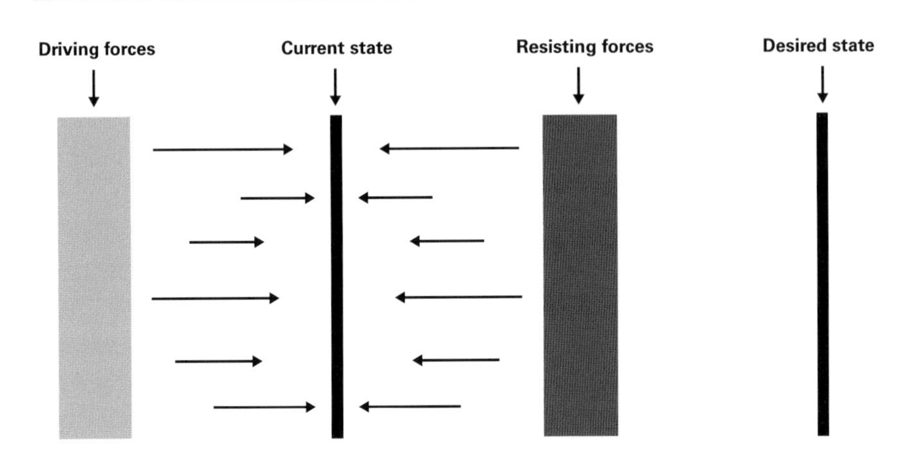




Putting various forces by each arrow then allows for the situation to be analysed. For instance, driving forces in the scenario might be the overwhelming demand from patients (or politicians), the presence of a new partner, the need to maintain practice list size and the fear of being 'behind the times'. Resisting forces might be an individuals' fear of change, anxiety about coping with family commitments, fear of employers' contractual obligations, a feeling that the practice is 'achieving' anyway (Lewin's 'equilibrium') and a feeling of comfort. Lewin would argue that it is best to look at the resistors, for example balancing one late evening with an early start but an early finish.

Another commonly used tool is the 'SWOT' analysis[5]– standing for Strengths, Weaknesses, Opportunities and Threats – which recognises that internal and external factors must be considered simultaneously. Using this tool, the relative advantages and disadvantages can be discussed. This is a very good way to get a group of people to brainstorm or 'shower thoughts' when discussing a problem. In allowing different individuals to voice enthusiasms and concerns, greater ownership of the problem and solutions can be discussed. It does however need good facilitation to stop over-analysis preventing a change.

### *Planning the change*

Both of the above tools can fool an individual into thinking that change is a simple, straightforward and linear process, and it can be made to look that way if a change process is broken down into sufficient steps.

Readiness and capability is a method of identifying which people need to be influenced to change and which people are ready to do so. Beckhard and Harris[6] suggest that the project manager should develop a chart (readiness–capability assessment chart) that identifies which individuals are critical to the change process and which are ready to change. By doing this, effort can be concentrated towards those who are essential first. In the case of the scenario, one of the partners could take the lead (see Chapter 10), by trying it out, and then return with an assessment of the pros and cons. Understanding each person's personal circumstances might also be useful, for instance acknowledging that a single mother with underage children is going to find it very difficult to do the early and late starts, and pick her children up from nursery. So perhaps a five-year plan to review things regularly should be implemented, making sure that the scenario is a win/win. Those who start early could lose an hour's working time, or having split shifts might reduce those that always book late and need to be seen at the end of the day.

Table 13.1 ○ ***Readiness–capability assessment chart, using the scenario as an example***

| Resistant to change | Uncomfortable with the change | Neutral | Comfortable with the change | Enthusiastic |
|---|---|---|---|---|
| Administrative staff | | | * | |
| | | | | Practice manager and newest partner |
| Oldest GP partner | | | | * |
| | | Nursing staff | * | |
| | | | Other partners | |
| | | | | Patients |

* Denotes the position that individuals need to reach in order to change.

There is a difference between 'commitment', 'enrolment' and 'compliance' when understanding how ready for change individuals are in an organisation. Senge[7] suggests that, although useful, it is not necessary to have equal and considerable commitment, aligning himself with Beckhard and Harris's model. He suggests there are a number of positions along a continuum, along which individuals will position themselves.

Table 13.2 ○ ***Senge's positions of commitment, enrolment and compliance***

| **Disposition** | **Players' response to change** |
|---|---|
| Commitment | Want to change and make it happen |
| Enrolment | Want to change and will work in given frameworks |
| Genuine compliance | See the virtue in the proposal and think about what is needed |
| Formal compliance | Can describe the benefits. Not hostile; do what is asked but no more |
| Grudging compliance | Do not accept proposal and do not go along with it. Do enough not to jeopardise own position |
| Non-compliance | Do not accept proposal and have nothing to lose by opposing it. Will not do what is asked |
| Apathy | Neither in support nor in opposition; just serving time |

*Source*: adapted from Senge.[7]

Chapter 15 goes into greater detail on project planning. In many ways instituting change is a small project. When looking at change a plan is needed.

- ▷ **Who** needs to be influenced first?
- ▷ **Who** needs to be influenced most and least?
- ▷ **How** should they be influenced?
- ▷ **How** should the organisation restructure itself to accommodate the change?
- ▷ **What** needs to be put in place to allow this to happen?
- ▷ **What** is the expected outcome?

This can be applied to the scenario, as follows.

WHO

- ▷ The need to get the partners who are in executive control on board.
- ▷ The need to talk to the partner most put off by change to do so first, and use the practice manager, who needs no persuading to help.

HOW

- ▷ Consider personal circumstances. Balance a late finish with an early one.
- ▷ Use the team to come up with solutions to cover a longer opening time.

WHAT

- ▷ Consider giving new staff contracts to cover longer hours and phasing the start over one or two years.
- ▷ Plan to keep to a realistic timetable and give feedback to patients to minimise frustration.



---

## Changing individuals

One of the earliest works into why humans change was carried out by sociologist Everett Rogers.[8] When his book *Diffusion of Innovations* was first published in 1962 it very quickly became a landmark work in its field. Rogers, through his observations, stated that individuals fell into distinct types, including *innovators* (who will change very rapidly), *early adopters* (who think a little more, but are ready for change), *late adopters* (who need to be more convinced) and *laggards* (who are slow to change but once on the path of change are slow to leave it). He described how any innovation (which is an idea, practice or object that is perceived to be new to an individual or unit of adoption) is communicated through certain channels among the members of a social system, and looks at change as a diffusion. Extrapolating his theory it is possible to see how a positive culture can aid an organisation's ability to change and develop. He also describes the powerful *opinion leaders* and *change agents* that can be in any group, society or organisation. Within the NHS it can be easy to see how these roles can be used. A respected consultant giving a well-researched lecture can act as a powerful opinion leader, then allowing the change agent (perhaps the PCT clinical governance facilitator) an easier time in changing attitudes to a related pathway of care. Somewhat more sinister are the tactics used by pharmaceutical representatives who 'detail' doctors in order to find out how easy they are to influence and what influence that doctor will have on his or her colleagues.[9]

GPs are very used to wanting to influence and change the behaviour of patients. There is a vast literature on how effective communication can help patients decide, but this is very much outside the scope of this chapter. Talking the same 'language', making an individual own some of the ideas, and making him or her feel 'empowered' to change are central to many models of communication. Prochaska and DiClemente's cycle of change is often taught to identify, and then move someone in, a direction of change. Although often quoted, it should be remembered that their 'transtheoretical model of the cycle of change' was first used in addictive behaviours.[10] They do however also point out that the ability to change will depend on an individual weighing up the pros and cons, and the individual's confidence in his or her own ability to change. This might be useful when looking to change an individual's behaviour by remembering to include reinforcement strategies in the change plan.



## Change in organisations

Change is rarely simple and linear, and is often difficult in healthcare organisations that are large and complex institutions. Change agents in the NHS use '*whole systems thinking*' to recognise that:

- there are multifactorial issues to consider, and the solutions will lie with more than one individual
- the organisation is an integrated 'living and dynamic structure', and solutions should reflect this
- there needs to be a recognition that there is a need to develop shared values, purposes and practices
- it is sometimes necessary to widen the interventions in order to bring together the perspectives of a wide range of stakeholders.[3]

Large-scale changes are often driven by national guidelines and will have whole teams of managers, administrators and clinicians to effect that change. Examples in the UK include National Service Frameworks, which set the standards and describe ways of working across the whole of healthcare provision, and guidelines from the National Institute of Health and Clinical Excellence, which will often evaluate new interventions, including the economic and social aspects of a change. Lastly it should not be forgotten that where change is needed there is a need for good leadership (see Chapter 10).

## Conclusion

Change is complex and in health care rarely involves one individual. Even when attempting to practice EBP there is an onus in today's corporate governance structures to not only ensure that the GP as an individual is using the best available evidence in treating the patient, but also that the whole team is doing it too. In a review of 44 reviews on changing behaviour[11] it was shown that there are no magic bullets, and that:

- ▷ most interventions are effective in some circumstances; none is effective in all
- ▷ a diagnostic analysis of the individual and the context should be analysed before selecting a method to alter individual behaviour
- ▷ interventions based on assessment of potential barriers are more likely to be effective
- ▷ multifaceted interventions are more useful than single interventions
- ▷ reminder systems are very useful
- ▷ audit, feedback and opinion leaders have mixed effects
- ▷ passive dissemination when used alone (memos, printed guidelines or emails) are unlikely to result in behaviour change but might raise awareness.

The GP in the scenario is well placed to undertake the change, given the opportunity to get to know his colleagues, to use the skills of his fellow collaborators in the change, in a culture that hopefully fosters change with a reduction in resistance.

*If you always do what you always did, you always get what you always got.*
(*Mark Twain*)

## Questions

1 ▷ What are the five steps of EBP?

2 ▷ From what academic disciplines does change management theory come from?

3 ▷ How does the research differ from scientific research?

4 ▷ What would a force field analysis look like?

5 ▷ What is a chart of readiness and capability to change, and how is it useful in assessing an organisation's ability to change?

**6** ▷ Which types of people in their readiness to change were described by Everett Rogers?

**7** ▷ How can Prochaska and DiClemente's research into addictive behaviour change be extrapolated to other behaviour change?

**8** ▷ How useful is passive dissemination of written material in influencing change?



## References

1 • Evidence-Based Working Group. Evidence-Based Medicine: a new approach to teaching the practice of medicine *Journal of the American Medical Association* 1992; **268**: 2420–5.

2 • Dawes M, Summerskill W, Glasziou P, *et al.* Sicily statement on evidence based practice *BMC Medical Education* 2005; **5(1)**.

3 • Iles V, Sutherland K. *Managing Change in the NHS: organisational change, a review for healthcare managers, professionals and researchers* London: National Co-ordinating Centre for NHS Service Delivery and Organisation R&D, 2001.

4 • Lewin K. *Field Theory in Social Science* New York: Harper & Row, 1951.

5 • Ansoff H. *Corporate Strategy: an analytic approach to business policy for growth and expansion* New York: McGraw-Hill, 1965.

6 • Beckhard R, Harris R. *Organisational Transitions: managing complex change* Wokingham: Addison-Wesley, 1987.

7 • Senge P. *The Fifth Discipline: the art and practice of the learning organisation* London: Doubleday/Century Business, 1990.

8 • Rogers E. *Diffusion of Innovations* (third edn) London: Collier Macmillan, 1983.

9 • Tonks A. Shortcuts: how pharmaceutical representatives change your behaviour *British Medical Journal* 2007; **334**: 1029 [taken from PLoS Med 2007:e150 doi:10.1371/journal.pmed.0040150].

10 • Prochaska J O, DiClemente C C, Norcross J C. In search of how people change: application to addictive behaviours *American Psychologist* 1992; **47**: 1102–14.

11 • NHS Centre for Reviews and Dissemination, Getting evidence into practice *Effective Health Care* 1999; **5(1)**: 1–16.

# Developing a business case

# 14

*Robert Cragg and Veronica Wilkie*

### *Scenario*

*You have settled into your practice, and have just completed a diploma in practical dermatology. Your local trust is struggling to meet its waiting time deadlines and your partners ask you if you are interested in putting together a business case to be a GP with a Special Interest (GPwSI) in dermatology. A number of the GPs you met whilst doing your course had been 'sponsored' by their Primary Care Trusts (PCTs) and were actively setting up these services on their own patches. The local trust is struggling to meet the demands of referrals within the current waiting time directives. You feel clinically able to do this and get on well with the local dermatologist, but have no idea how you should go about writing a business case.*



## Introduction

A business case is a plan of how a proposed service development will look and include a breakdown of all the costs involved. The benefits of the proposed service should be identified in the widest possible sense, looking at the impact on patient care locally and across the wider healthcare community, as well as the impact on staff, buildings and competing services. The business case is a formal document that is required to be circulated and approved by key stakeholders and commissioners in order to get the service development off the ground. This chapter will look at what makes a good business case using the example detailed above.

## Business case contents

Any business case is specific to its target audience. A GP might well look at writing a smaller and more localised business case to present to the practice at a partners' meeting, looking more at the costs and benefits to the practice patients and as an organisation. Once this is agreed, the business case would then have to be developed further to be considered by the commissioning body (which might be a PCT or a commissioning consortium).

#### *Part one: why? To respond to national/local policy and health needs*

Much of health care is currently concerned with waiting times. Components of dermatology can be delivered easily in the community and some aspects can be identified as needing specialist secondary or tertiary input. Some conditions can be managed by an appropriately trained GP or nurse. There are very specific guidelines on good practice when setting up such a service and these can be found on the Department of Health (DoH) website, www.dh.gov.uk/en/Publicationsandstatistics/Publications/Publications Legislation/DH_074792.

Since the late 1990s the NHS has been looking at better use of skills of all healthcare professionals so that specialists have enough time to provide complex care, and that more straightforward conditions can be managed closer to the patients in the community. The term 'Practitioner with a Specialist Interest' includes nurses, physios and other healthcare workers, as well as GPs. In the case of our scenario the business case would have to state the need for such a service locally and might include evidence on problems meeting wait times from secondary care, rurality, patient choice and cost savings to the practice under Practice-Based Commissioning.



Certain specialties lend themselves to specific population demographics; for instance, inner-city populations often require enhanced services for specialties such as diabetes, substance misuse and cardiovascular disease. Whatever the case, consideration of the following issues is essential:

- ▷ fulfilling national and/or local targets
- ▷ achieving quality or safety advancement
- ▷ improving annual health check ratings
- ▷ meeting National Institute for Health and Clinical Excellence (NICE) and National Service Frameworks (NSF) guidelines
- ▷ responding to patient surveys or feedback
- ▷ generating income/financial efficiency.

It is key to consider the health needs as they are perceived by patients and commissioners before proceeding to business case development.

#### *Part two: what?*

Every successful business case looks at a wide range of service models, looking at more than just cost provision. Patient safety, clinical governance issues and patient convenience might be a reason for choosing an option that is not the cheapest. The options a PCT might consider in this scenario are:

- ▷ another dermatologist
- ▷ expanded secondary care clinics in the hospital
- ▷ nurse-led clinics
- ▷ purchase of services from an adjacent NHS provider
- ▷ purchase of services from a non-NHS provider
- ▷ GPwSI service
- ▷ a mixture of the above service models
- ▷ no change in which treatment targets fail to be met; outpatient waits require extra funding under secondary waiting list initiatives.

A practice looking to rationalise outpatient costs might consider the benefits of providing the dermatology service through a GPwSI, which might also benefit practice profits or offset the costs of providing extra services.



***Part three: who and when?***

Proposed service by the GP in the scenario is two sessions a month, of three hours, seeing nine (five new, four follow-ups), and one session per month as a clinical assistant in consultant-led hospital dermatology clinic. The GP sessions will include: cryotherapy; diagnostic biopsies; diagnosis and management of chronic skin conditions; and some minor surgery. Current good practice also suggests a minimum of 15 hours of Continuing Professional Development (CPD) a year and if diagnosis of skin cancers is included attendance at a minimum of four multidisciplinary team oncology meetings. Whatever the model of care, consideration of the following is important. You must:

- ▷ align your business with current or future organisational targets/ objectives
- ▷ respond to current policy directives or organisational deficiencies
- ▷ demonstrate that there is a market need for your development
- ▷ be future proof
- ▷ take account of competitors' position
- ▷ have support of wider health economy.

When assigning a lead or a team to the newly proposed service, the following needs to be considered:

- ▷ who will take responsibility for the service?
- ▷ when will the benefits be realised?

- who will monitor and audit?
- a clear timeline is necessary for delivering the development
- who would have to make changes to how they work? Who will need training? Who will maintain?

### *Part four: how much? Consideration of all capital and revenue costs involved*

Before considering a new service development the current costs of existing service provision need to be clearly identified.

For the purposes of this chapter the potential costs and income from a GPwSI service will be expanded on. In reality other options would also have to be detailed. It is important that a contingency fund or an agreed evaluation of costs is built into your financial model. Also a risk assessment on activity assumptions is vital.



Table 14.1 ○ ***Current cost of a routine dermatology outpatient attendance (estimated costs only)***

| Outpatient specialty code | Outpatient specialty name | Adult first-attendance tariff (£) | Adult follow-up-attendance tariff (£) | Child (U17) first-attendance tariff (£) | Child (U17) follow-up attendance tariff (£) |
|---|---|---|---|---|---|
| 330 | Dermatology outpatients | 115 | 57 | 126 | 69 |

| HRG code | HRG name | Elective spell tariff (£) | Elective long-stay trimpoint (days) | Non-elective spell tariff (£) |
|---|---|---|---|---|
| J44 | Minor dermatological conditions or benign tumours | 583 | 1 | 1394 |

*Source*: Department of Health. *National Tariff 2006/07*, 31 January 2006, www.dh.gov.uk/en/Publicationsandstatistics/Publications/PublicationsPolicyAndGuidance/DH_4127649. Crown copyright material is reproduced with the permission of the Controller of OPSI.

Table 14.2 ○ ***Sessional costs to practice (estimates for illustration only)***

| | |
|---|---|
| Locum cost for replacement of GP time lost including CPD and MDT | £200 |
| Secretarial costs | £20 |
| Stationery and postage | £5 |
| Consumables including liquid nitrogen | £40 |
| Maintenance and electricity costs | £15 |
| One-hour nursing | £20 |
| Reception time | £20 |
| Travel and storage for consumables including liquid nitrogen | £15 |

Table 14.3 ○ ***Yearly costs***

| | |
|---|---|
| PCT contingency for changes in year | £2000 |
| CPD | £500 |



## COST / BENEFIT EXERCISE

The cost to the practice of five new referrals and four follow-ups at the local hospital/acute trust might be:

$5 \times 115 + 4 \times 57 = £803$ plus the minor surgery costs of £1749 for three patients.

The income proposed to the practice is £60 per patient. Based on nine patients a session the practice gets £540 for each session, minor surgery costs to be included in the £60 fee until evaluation at three months.

Overall the proposed savings for each session for the commissioning body in outpatient and minor ops costs is £1749 −335 which is £1414. The proposed profit to the practice for the session is 540 −335 = £205 (annually at two a month and allowing for holiday it would be £2050 minus any CPD costs etc.), with just over £1000 to offset the cost of employing a locum to cover the shortfall in net income received for the clinical assessment post.

The non-financial costs for consideration are:

- loss of continuity as one of the GPs is taken out of normal surgery time
- duplication of costs when a GPwSI has to refer on to the hospital

- ▷ benefits including increased skills within the practice
- ▷ a more local service for patients.

Table 14.4 ○ ***Other costs to consider***

| **Capital** | **Revenue** |
|---|---|
| Construction costs | Capital charges |
| Professional fees | Pay costs |
| Furniture and equipment | Maintenance |
| IT and telecom | Ongoing care |
| Commissioning costs | Acknowledge Payment by Results |



Obviously if the service proposed is not looking at saving costs but incurring new costs that cannot be clawed back from elsewhere, then a clear idea of where this funding is coming from and how long the funding stream will continue is needed. Possible options for new funding include:

- ▷ talking to neighbouring and local commissioners to seek their interest
- ▷ private, community and public-sector partners.

### *Part five: marketing*

Any new service or change in service will need to be advertised. Those who refer into the service and those who support it will need to know how the change impacts on them. Sending out a circular or flyer might have limited impact as it would be lost in the deluge of such material that all doctors receive. Your strategy should include meeting and discussing the new service with colleagues and ideally a good business case should make provision for this to ensure no loss of day-to-day appointment availability.

### *Part six: evaluation*

Business cases should detail how and when the proposed service will be reviewed in line with its objectives. Full consideration of clinical governance connotations is critical. Peer reviews of finance and service quality should be built in as standard with a financial and time cost of the evaluations built into the figures.

## WHAT MAKES BUSINESS CASES SUCCEED?

The case discussed above is based on a real project that was successfully implemented. It appealed to commissioners fulfilling national target objectives and sound financial management. It has been evaluated and some of the costs were changed on review of the experience of clinics and the amount of time and the costs of consumables incurred by minor surgery. The ease of which the cost changes were accepted was greatly helped by a comprehensive business case discussion at the outset.

## WINNING WHYS – FOUR MAIN WAYS

**1** ▷ On patient safety grounds where a high 'risk' is demonstrated.

**2** ▷ New ventures must generate profit or break even.

**3** ▷ Enhancing current services to meet the practice or trust's current targets and enhancing current services to meet local unmet patient need.

**4** ▷ Bidding for national or regional tender contracts to provide a new/ expanded service with ring-fenced monies.



## ASSESSING RISK: WHAT IS THE SEVERITY AND WHAT IS THE LIKELIHOOD?

When developing a business case, 'risks' that any organisation might consider are:

▷ potential injury and harm to patients, staff, public
▷ disruption to service continuity
▷ breach of quality
▷ potential litigation
▷ damage to trust reputation/publicity
▷ must be evidenced from risk registers, complaints and incident forms
▷ loss of income causing financial deficit, through loss of activity or increased competition.

Any of these risks should be assessed and a considered measure of likelihood of occurrence and estimated impact across a given scale, e.g. low, slight, moderate, severe, catastrophic, or numerically 1–5.

Within the NHS a commissioning or provider organisation should have a *set business case pro forma* that you need to familiarise yourself with. Each locality will have a prescribed and agreed system for grading risk to which applicants must adhere.

## THE PATH OF A TYPICAL BUSINESS CASE

The typical business case takes a considerable time to be approved. The process can be frustrating and bureaucratic with perseverance the order of the day. If successful your business case needs to progress through several key stages discussed below. This example assumes that the GP will take the lead for developing the plan, but in reality another member of the primary care team might take the lead, using the GP as the clinical lead.

### Stage one: development and approval of the business case in the practice or directorate

This can take up to 2–3 months. The GP works up the business case with the practice manager; the costs and ability of the team to undertake the service are fully scrutinised in-house. The GP then presents the business case to the partners. There is liaison with all stakeholders and partners, including open dialogue with secondary care.



### Stage two: submission of case to commissioners for consideration of case

This might take three months or more. The commissioning lead within the practice takes the submission to the Practice-Based Commissioning (PBC) board. The business case goes to the PCT board/commissioning team for consideration. If approved, a review date and financial agreement to pay needs to be formalised. You should *always* get approval in writing. If rejected, the proposed service model might require revisions or even a complete return to the blackboard.

The timings reflect the complexity of the case and the number of stakeholders involved. The more players there are the more protracted the process, e.g. if the business case involves referral from other practices or income from multiple PCTs.

### Stage three: implementation, training and marketing

This can take 6–12 months depending of the size of the proposal. To make the service go live, plans, procedures and protocols need to be established and put into place. Marketing and training strategies need to be implemented from day one to ensure activity levels and patient safety respectively.

## Summary

Writing a business case requires:

- ▷ financial realism
- ▷ appreciation of risk
- ▷ innovation and lateral thinking
- ▷ appreciation of best practice
- ▷ persistence and networking
- ▷ careful planning
- ▷ time
- ▷ enormous energy and commitment
- ▷ political and persuasion skills.

Business cases are specific to the project being considered but might have a prescribed format provided by funding bodies. This chapter has summarised some of the key aspects to consider when developing a business case.

Proper business case planning should include the wider costs to the practice and not merely be evaluated in terms of increased revenue.



## Questions

1 ▷ What is a business case?

2 ▷ What are the two main components for calculating risk?

3 ▷ What are examples of revenue should a business case consider?

4 ▷ What are the components of a business case?

5 ▷ What makes business cases successful? Provide four examples.

6 ▷ Who needs to see and approve a business case?

7 ▷ Who should develop a business case?

8 ▷ What are examples of capital costs that a business case should consider?

9 ▷ What is a typical timeline for a primary care business case from start to finish?

# Project management

# 15

*Jonathan Howes*

### *Scenario*

*You have been asked to look at building a very large extension for your practice. The council is willing to sell some waste land by the side of the practice. The Primary Care Trust (PCT) is keen for space to be available for its community staff, as well as a dental access centre and pharmacy.*

*Unfortunately your practice manager has suddenly had to take some unplanned leave for ill health reasons and you have agreed to step in. The office manager who is acting as the practice manager asks you if you have any project-planning experience. You had no idea that there was any specific need to 'plan' a project in any particular way.*



## Introduction

This chapter offers an introduction to key processes of project management. Projects will vary in size, can be tangible or intangible and the scope and variety can be enormous, e.g. house building, IT solutions, etc. The common trait with all projects is that they should be *a temporary venture undertaken to create a new service or product*. An area of work that is ongoing with no finish date should be described as 'business as usual' rather than a project.

## Some background information about building premises in primary care

Most GPs will be involved in a building move or extension at least once in a working life. This project is not about 'how to' extend or build but uses a building project as an example. One of the hardest steps to take in any such scenario is the ability to get money for the project. Historically buildings were agreed by the Primary Care Organisation (PCO) using *cost rent*. This was a formula that determined the size and cost of a build. It historically allowed buildings to be built when the commercial rates were insufficient to pay off a loan, historically held by the doctors in the practice. The *notional rent* was the cost per square metre a practice would get on a commercial rent. If this exceeded cost rent, practices would use this to calculate the building cost, or switch over to a notional rent reimbursement as the value increased with inflation. As with the rest of the UK economy and reflecting the increasing sophistication of healthcare premises, there has been a change away from simple 'cost rent buildings' with organisations outside the NHS building the premises (*Private Finance Initiative* [PFI]) after negotiating a rent with the PCO. Although rented, these premises are still very often built to the specification of the practice, but often also include requirements reflecting wider community need.

*NHS Local Improvement Finance Trusts* (LIFT) are a joint venture between the private sector, local NHS, local authority and other stakeholders (GPs, dentists and pharmacists, for example), to join together as a limited company in order to finance a building designed and commissioned by the wider local health economy. The steps described by the Department of Health (DoH) are:



1. ▷ the local health economy looks at what it needs to deliver local health care, by forming a Strategic Service Development Plan
2. ▷ a partner from the private sector is then sought (via competitive 'procurement') to set up the LIFT company, which is a partnership between the private sector and all the public sector participants
3. ▷ this company then enters into a 20 or 25 year undertaking to deliver the partnering services, i.e. to build, maintain and operate the service.

As a response to the increasingly complex funding and occupation of primary care buildings, professional 'primary care development consultants' exist to act as project managers and to advise practices.

For the purposes of illustration this chapter will assume a simple model of the practice owning the premises and extension, and therefore negotiating the increased rent with its local PCO.

---

## Project management

The Association of Project Management define project management as the:

> *planning, monitoring and control of all aspects of a project and the motivation of all those involved in it to achieve the project objectives on time and to the specified cost, quality and performance.*[1]

An alternative definition could be:

*The controlled implementation of defined change.*

Project management has evolved and like many business processes has its own terminology and jargon. This chapter aims to look at the terminology, explain the processes and products, and then use the scenario set as an example. The chapter uses the building of an extension as an illustration; it is not intended to be a chapter on how to extend a practice, and is hopefully an introduction to the stages and terminology used. Any of these principles can be adapted to any project a GP might find him or herself involved with, for example Practice-Based Commissioning, starting to be a training practice or even appointing a new partner or accountant. The smaller the project the easier it will be; the larger or more complex projects require more detail and planning.



## Project management methodology

A number of project management best-practice methods have been devised to enable effective project management.

A very widely used method, in the NHS, UK government and the private sector is PRINCE (***PR****ojects* ***IN*** ***C****ontrolled* ***E****nvironments*). PRINCE was originally a standard for all government information system projects and PRINCE 2 was launched in 1996, providing guidance for all types of project. PRINCE 2's methodology is process-driven rather than time-driven. The processes define the activities that must be carried out during the project. The eight PRINCE 2 processes cover the project cycle from project start-up to completion.

An alternative to process-driven project management methods is *reactive/adaptive methods*. The philosophy of adaptive project management methodologies is that observed challenges cannot be fully addressed by the traditional process-driven methodology. They instead focus on maximising the team's ability to respond in an agile manner to emerging challenges.

Not all projects are successful and the above processes are used to maximise the chances of success. Before these processes are explained in more detail it is important to keep in mind the main reasons why some projects fail:

**1** ▷ failure to specify the project properly

**2** ▷ lack of ownership

**3** ▷ insufficient skilled and experienced personnel to deliver the project

4 ▷ lack of user involvement

5 ▷ inadequate reporting and decision-making processes.

---

## Setting up a project

### *1. Business case*

A business case proposal for business change must be justified in terms of costs and benefits. For any project to exist there needs to be a basic business requirement, which should have clearly defined deliverables (measurable results to be achieved) and benefits (measurable benefits to the organisation, e.g. increased income, better trained staff, better care for patients). Each end-point and benefit of the project should meet the SMART test:[2]



- ***S***pecific ○ clearly described and defined
- ***M***easurable ○ able to measure with metrics
- ***A***chievable ○ with the resources and skills available
- ***R***ealistic ○ attainable with current knowledge
- ***T***ime-bound ○ having a completion date.

These must be the focus of the project throughout its lifespan. If a project loses sight of the business case, the project should be re-evaluated.

### *2. Setting the scope*

The scope of a project is the totality of the work needed to complete the project. The scope should be defined together with the customer (i.e. the person or organisation commissioning the work) and project board (those involved in delivering and leading the project) during the project start-up phase. Scope should be defined:

- broadly enough to add value for the customer
- narrowly enough to be achievable with the resources, skill and time available
- in a meaningful way that is consistent with the project's objectives and can be easily communicated.[3]

### *3. The project initiation document*

Before a project is launched a document needs to be created that will allow the decision-makers/project board to initiate the project. This document is known as the *Project Initiation Document* or 'PID'. This document's purpose is to bring together the key information needed to start the project, the 'who, why, what, when and how'.

This document acts as a reference point throughout the project for both the customer and the project team, and contains elements such as the project goals, a financial business case and an assessment of risk.

### *4. Creating the project team*

The size of your project team would depend of the size of the project you will be undertaking, but the fundamental principle is that you will need someone to undertake the planning and someone to make the decisions.

The decision-makers on a project are known as the project board, and it is the project board who are ultimately responsible for the project and its direction. PRINCE 2 suggests that three main roles should be present on the project board:

- **executive** ○ represents the business interests (customer)
- **senior user** ○ represents the group who will be using the final product. Ensures the products meet the user requirements and provide the expected user benefits
- **senior supplier** ○ responsible for achieving the results required by the senior user and is responsible for the quality of all products delivered by the supplier.



---

### Project manager

The project manager is responsible for the day-to-day running of the project on behalf of the project board. The project manager ensures the required products are created to the specified quality within set timeframe and financial constraints. In the case of the scenario this might well be the practice manager, who will manage the project from the practice's point of view, but might be an external consultant or PCO manager in some cases.

---

### Specialist team managers

Depending on the size of the project you are undertaking you might not need team managers, and the project manager might be able to handle the tasks and activities alone.

For complex or specialist projects team managers play an important role. The project manager might appoint a team manager to be responsible for a certain work package/activity for which he or she does not have the specialist knowledge, e.g. for software development. When looking at the scenario, one of the doctors might work with the practice manager to ensure the clinical rooms are appropriate, a nurse look at infection control issues and the reception manager examine patient flow within the proposed build.

---

## Project support

The size of the project support team is normally determined by the size of the project. For smaller projects the project manager might be his or her own project support, but larger projects will need larger project structures. This role can be administrative, supporting the project manager by keeping project documentation up to date, arranging meetings, etc. They can also be specialists providing technical expertise.



In the scenario described above there are several projects that can be divided up:

1 ▷ the planning and design of the building, and the financial arrangements of the building

2 ▷ the commissioning and construction of the building

3 ▷ the move into the building and the patient and staff service continuity

4 ▷ looking at adopting and changing staff and service practice when the building is fully operated.

Clearly the practice will be very involved in steps 1, 3 and 4. The construction of the building will require the architect, developers and construction company to manage this process; the practice will obviously be involved but less so in the project.

Looking at the proposed project, the first step might start with the *business case*. The practice will need to put a business case to the PCT, ensuring that the costs of the rent (if a developer is building) or the bank loan (if the practice partnership is going to own the building) can be met. Any other occupiers of the building space, for example pharmacies, dental services or PCT-employed community staff, will need to be involved. An example of the SMART breakdown might be:

- ▷ ***S**pecific* – to build a healthcare facility that serves the local population to deliver all the locality primary healthcare needs by the medical practice and PCT-employed staff
- ▷ ***M**easurable* – the end building should be built and be big enough to house the staff that currently occupy cramped premises at several locations. It should be accessible to all patients, including those with disabilities
- ▷ ***A**chievable* – it should be built to be fit for twenty-first-century primary health care and within the budget available
- ▷ ***R**ealistic* – there is a considerable body of expertise as many primary care facilities have undergone new builds using a wide number of funding streams (owner occupied, PFI or LIFT funded), such that the project is realistic
- ▷ ***T**ime-bound* – the completion date should be no more than x months for the planning and design, added to the projected build time for the building.



---

## Planning a project

The majority of projects are completed late and over budget. Project plans if done thoroughly enough can help to minimise the effects of delay.

What should be in a project plan?

The project plan is used to determine the amount of resources required for the project – both finance and people – and the length of time the project will take. This will help you measure the progress of the project. All plans should have approval from the decision-makers/project board.

According to the PRINCE 2 methodology a plan should contain the following elements:

- ▷ the products to be produced
- ▷ the activities needed to create those products
- ▷ the activities needed to validate the quality of products
- ▷ the resources and time needed for all relevant activities
- ▷ the dependencies between activities
- ▷ the external dependencies for the delivery of information, products or services
- ▷ when activities will occur
- ▷ the points at which progress will occur
- ▷ the agreed tolerances.

## Levels of plan

A project plan is not necessarily one large complex plan with all the above elements. Rather it should be a number of plans for each component/stage of the project. PRINCE 2 proposes three levels of plan, the *project plan*, the *stage plan* and the *team plan*. The lower the level of plan the more detail it should contain and the shorter the timeframe.

### *Project plan*

This provides the overview of the project. It highlights the key products, resource requirements and cost. It should also highlight the key control points of the project. For instance in the scenario the project plan 'overview' might be that the extension is to be built, allowing for five extra consulting rooms, a waiting room, a pharmacy, a larger reception area and ten new offices (three for the practice and seven for the community staff). The resources would include time for the project manager and PCT to agree on the budget (for example £750,000), as well as additional fees such as architect costs etc.



### *Stage plan*

The stage plan is used for the basis of control within a stage. It identifies all the products that are created within the stage and defines stage tolerances, reporting and control points.

Stages identified for the extension would be:

1 ▷ availability of purchase of the land

2 ▷ design of the building and planning permission

3 ▷ ensuring cost of the design does not exceed the budget set and that all the different components of the budget are identified

4 ▷ patient flow and service continuity during the build.

### *Team plan*

The need for team plans will be determined by the size and complexity of the project. These are often needed if there are specialist skills required or external contractors.

These team plans would obviously involve the contractors and the architect, as well as plans for the new occupants of the building.

### ***Exception plan***

When a project exceeds its agreed tolerances an exception plan will replace a stage or team plan. An exception plan should detail all the actions required to remedy the effect of the deviation from tolerance.

An example of this might be if a structural problem is identified with the existing building that requires remedy before the extension is built, or if certain planning requirements demand a redesign. In a good project plan these possibilities will have been thought out at the earliest possible opportunity so as to minimise delay and cost.

### ***Communication plan***

Communications should be planned like every other task on a project. The communication plan should define the means and frequency of communication between all interested parties of the project.

Where a practice is 'commissioning' the extension, there should be a clear mechanism for the architect, builders or developers to contact one person with any problems. This would ideally be someone who is accessible, has enough seniority to make decisions on small matters and has the authority to convene a meeting of the 'executive' body. In the scenario, the practice manager would be better than a busy GP. In his or her absence the office manager should be empowered, with the lead GP communicating and supporting him or her until the practice manager returns. There should be a defined time for the partnership to meet and discuss important issues that arise.



### ***Work breakdown structure/product breakdown structure***

Work/product breakdown structures are techniques that use hierarchical tree structures to determine the total scope of the project and the sub-products needed to create the final project. The Project Management Institute states:

> *the Work Breakdown Structures includes 100% of the work defined by the project scope and captures ALL deliverables – internal, external, interim – in terms of the work to be completed.*[4]

A work/product breakdown structure should be completed before estimating and scheduling occurs.

Figure 15.1 ○ ***Example of work/product breakdown structure***

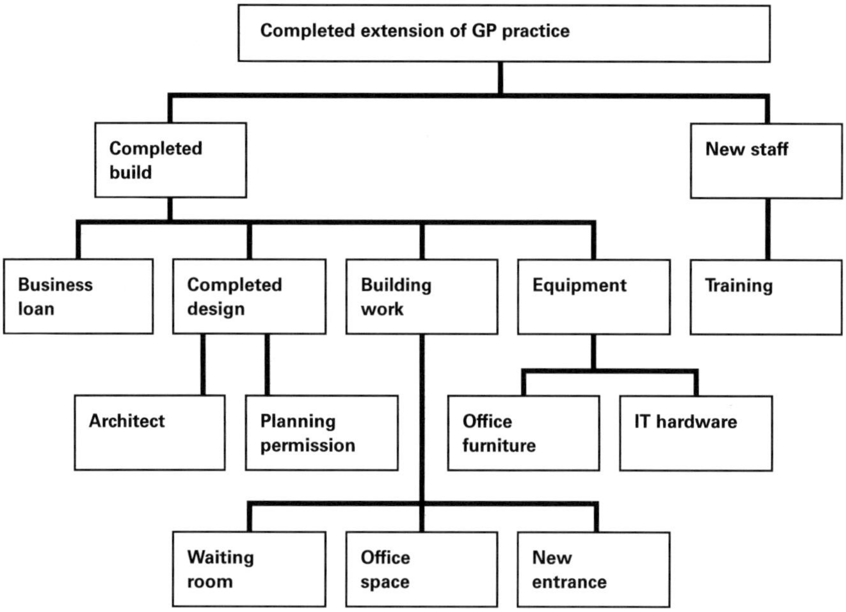

## Estimating and scheduling

Estimating:

*is the process which identifies the cost and time it will take to complete a project.*

Although estimating will not guarantee accuracy it can provide an overall view of the resources needed. Estimating can be made more accurate through using previous project data and the experiences of the project management team, and also the views and knowledge of experts for particular parts of the project, e.g. architects, electricians, software developers.

Estimating should be determined by the level of plan you are estimating on. A project plan should contain estimates for the entire project, broken down across the stages. Estimating a stage plan should contain estimates for each product that are then built up into the plan.

PRINCE 2 defines two steps to estimating:

▷ **identify resource types required** ○ the specific skills required depending on the type of project, e.g. the skills and experiences of the staff needed, finance, money and equipment

▷ **estimate the effort required for each activity by resource type** ○ at the planning stage this can only be approximate.

Although estimating is a series of assumptions it should enable the decision-makers to make valid decisions and set appropriate tolerances for the project.

A schedule:

*is a plan with the dates for the work fixed and accepted by the customer.*

Schedules can be created manually or using project management software such as Microsoft Project or Primavera Project Planner. Looking at the complexity of the extension project it becomes clear why a good software programme can help in even this relatively small project. A 'critical path method' can also be used for project scheduling. This method constructs a model of the product using:

▷ all the activities and products
▷ the time that each activity would take to complete (start and end times)
▷ the dependency between activities and products.

By defining these issues the method highlights those activities that are critical to the completion of the project and those activities that are less critical and have 'float time'. The critical path method allows the project team to prioritise the activities and effectively manage the project.

Project schedules can be graphically represented by the use of Gantt charts (see Table 15.1, p. 214).



---

## Risk

The management of risk should be a major factor to be considered in any project. However, a certain amount of risk is inevitable if a project is to achieve its objectives. The project management team must control and contain by taking action to keep the project's exposure to the risk to a minimum and in a cost-effective way.

PRINCE 2 has six steps in the risk management/risk analysis cycle that should be considered when handling risk.

### *1. Identify the risks*

What category the risk is will affect how it is handled. Categories of risk include economic, political, technical and organisational.

Table 15.1 ○ ***A Gantt chart of a project schedule***

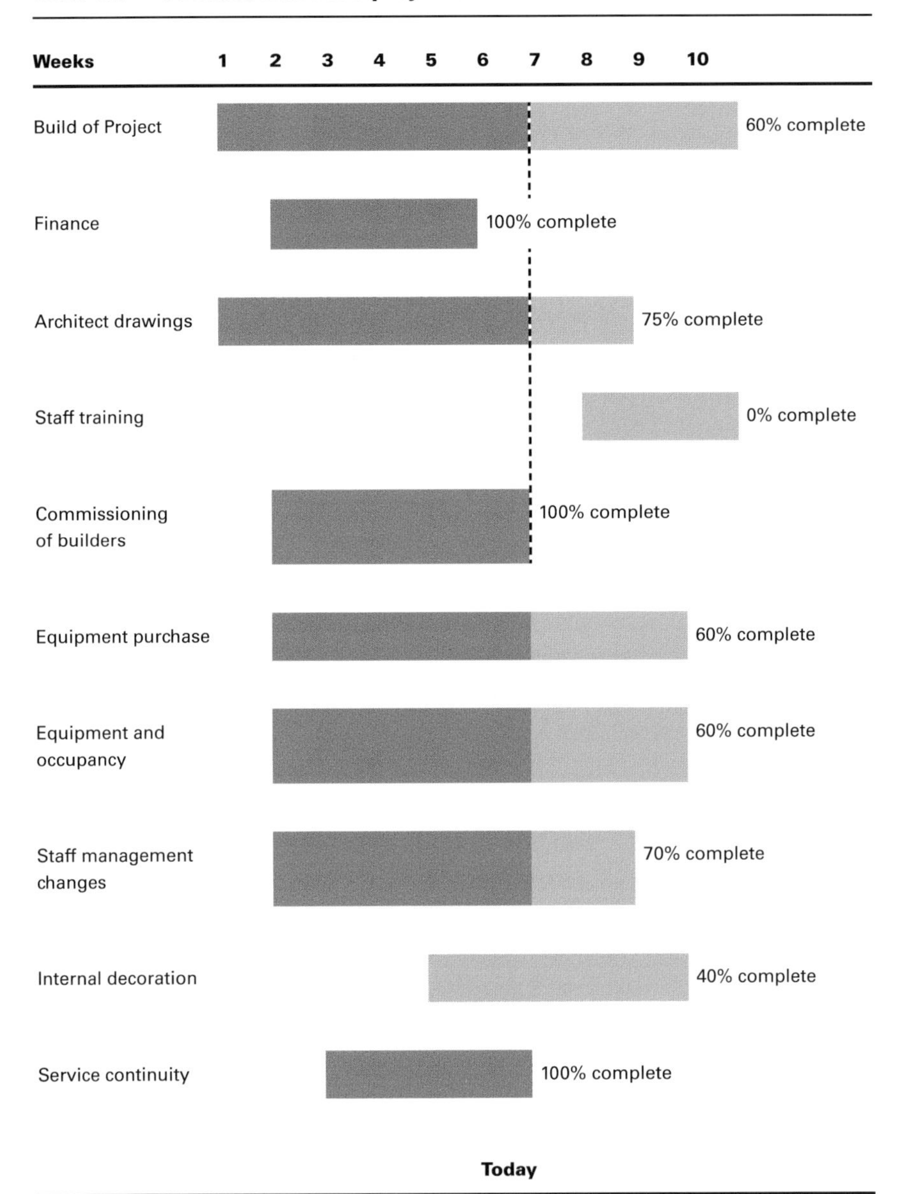


*Note*: estimates and schedules will change over the course of the project. As the extension is being built further costs, risks and changes might have to be incorporated into the initial schedule and estimates. As part of the estimation for a project from which you have little previous experience to draw, a 'change budget' and/or a contingency budget should be created in order to pay for the new changes or risks that are discovered.

### *2. Evaluate the risks*

The probable and possible impact of risks needs to be considered, including interdependencies and external factors. Elements that should be considered when evaluating the impact of risk include the impact on cost, resources, quality and time.

### *3. Identify suitable response*

- ▷ **Contingency** ○ the risk might have been foreseen and planned for, and a 'contingency budget' to carry out the response might be in place.
- ▷ **Reduce** ○ control the risk to reduce the likelihood of it happening or its impact on the project.
- ▷ **Accept** ○ impact of risk is minimum and to acceptable level.
- ▷ **Prevent** ○ do activity differently in order to remove the risk.
- ▷ **Transfer** ○ move risk to a third party such as insurance company.



### *4. Select response*

The response to the risk should be proportional to the impact and probability of risk, and must be a cost-effective response.

### *5. Plan and resource*

Once the response has been selected a plan of action will need to be developed that should be incorporated into the stage and project plans. The decision-makers of the project should give approval for the risk management plan.

### *6. Monitor and report*

The monitoring and reporting of the risk action is needed to identify changes in the risk status and to ensure the risk is being managed properly. The creation of a risk log should enable the management of risk to be recorded and monitored regularly.

*For the scenario of building an extension there might be a number of different categories of risk for you to identify and manage. The risk of the walls collapsing in the build could be considered unlikely but its impact on the project would be high. The impact of a delay in the installation of electrics and plumbing is more common but would not affect the project so dramatically. The creation of a risk register to log all the risks you identify will help you manage and monitor them successfully.*

## Managing/controlling the project

There are four key areas that a project manager is responsible for managing.

### *1. Controls*

The project team uses controls to enable decision-making during the project. The establishment of control helps ensure that the project is creating the required products, is being carried out on schedule and remains linked to the business case. PRINCE 2 states that controls ensure that each level of the project management team can:

- ▷ monitor progress
- ▷ compare and achieve plans
- ▷ review plans and options against future situations
- ▷ detect problems and identify risks
- ▷ initiate corrective action
- ▷ authorise further work.



Project controls can be either event-driven or time-driven. Event-driven controls are those that occur after a specific event has taken place, such as at an end of a project stage. Time-driven controls can be events such as regular progress reports.

### *2. Project stages*

A key control for the project management team is the creation of project stages during the planning stage. Stages should be created at specific points of the project where the project board needs to make key decisions before a further commitment of resources. Stages also allow the project board to review the progress of the project to date, review the risks and authorise the next stage of the project. Smaller projects might only have two stages, project initiation and the project itself, while larger more complex projects might have many stages.

### *3. Tolerance*

No project will go 100 per cent to plan. Therefore the decision-makers of the project might wish to determine levels of tolerance. Tolerance is the allowable deviation from a plan without having to bring the deviation to the attention of the decision-makers of the project.

The project board might set tolerances for the project manager to work to, and in turn the project manager might set tolerances for the team managers to work to. When a tolerance seems likely to be exceeded, the level of management must refer the matter to the next level up. New tolerances might be set as long as they are within the overall tolerance of the project/stage of project.

There are various different elements in the definition of tolerance. The two standard elements are *cost* and *time*. Tolerance can be set for both over and under cost and time. It should be represented by actual figures – a defined amount of time or money – rather than percentages.

Tolerances can also be set for other factors of the project. Examples of other areas that could have set tolerances would be risk and scope. How much risk is the project board prepared to allow? Scope tolerance can be defined as essential and desirable products.

With the project board setting tolerances and approving the project/stage plan it allows the concept of 'management by exception'. This allows the project manager to run the project on a day-to-day basis without progress meetings with the board, as long as the project stays within the agreed tolerances.



### 4. Reporting

Each level of the project management team can monitor and control the project through time-driven reporting controls. A project should have a communication plan; this is an important control as it identifies who needs to give and receive information about the project, and also defines the frequency with which they receive the communication.

Various types of report can be used during the project to manage, monitor and control the project.

- ▷ ***Highlight reports*** enable the project manager to update the project board (and other stakeholders) on the current status of the project. They should contain current project achievements, expected achievements in the next period and an overview of any issues and risks with suggestions on how to resolve them.
- ▷ ***Checkpoint reports*** are created by team managers to inform the project manager of the status of the work they are carrying out. They enable the project manager to check the progress against the team plan.
- ▷ ***Exception reports*** are produced when a stage, team or project plan is expected to exceed its agreed tolerances. They are prepared to inform the next level of management of the situation.
- ▷ ***End of stage reports*** are a summary of the stage and are used by the project board to approve the next stage, amend the stage or even stop the project.

- ▷ ***Project end reports*** are created to inform stakeholders on how well the project has performed against its original plan and scope.

## Change management

Every project undertaken is likely to change to some degree. Both the scope and the end product of the project are likely to change. The response should be not to reject all changes but to manage the changes through 'change management' or 'change control'. How to 'manage change' is outside the scope of this chapter and is covered in Chapter 13, but worth a mention as it is vital to the success of the project.

The most likely source of change is the customer wishing to add additional requirements or improve on the projects, in order to expand the scope. These are known as 'requests for change'. Change might also be created by a failure of the project team or supplier to meet one of the user's requirements. This is known as an 'off-specification change'.



PRINCE 2 considers each type of change as a project issue. The first step PRINCE 2 recommends for 'change control' is to prioritise the change.

- ▷ Is the change vital to the project?
- ▷ Is it nice to have but not vital?
- ▷ Is it a cosmetic change?

Once the change has been prioritised an impact analysis should be carried out to determine the impact on project and stage plans, tolerances, business case, risks and the effort it would take to carry out the change. It is important that there is a balance between the advantages of carrying out the change, and the time, cost and risks of implementing the change. With the likelihood of changes it might be advisable to plan ahead and incorporate a 'change budget' into your project planning.

Both 'requests for change' and 'off-specification change' should be authorised by the project board. They might delegate this responsibility to a change authority with a budget to carry out these changes.

*How a project manager controls a project is dependent on how involved the decision-makers/project board wish to be on a project. They might wish to be involved in every decision or be prepared to manage by exception.*

## Closing a project

Perhaps the most overlooked process, but one of the most important, is closing or ending a project. As projects have a defined objective it means they should not go on indefinitely. A clearly defined end to a project enables the project team to take stock of its achievements and experiences, and allows any unachieved goals to be identified so they can be addressed.

When closing a project the project management team should ensure that all expected products have been handed over and accepted by the customer, there has been formal acceptance by the project board and if necessary support and maintenance requirements defined.

The project team should evaluate the project against its initial business case and definition; this provides lessons learnt for future projects and any follow-on recommendations.

Not all projects are completed; the project board might decide that a project no longer meets the required business benefits. The project board have the power to do this at any stage of the project and will use the regular reports from the project manager to validate the project.

*Once the extension to the practice has been built, the project management team must obtain sign-off from both the customer and project board. If the project is not closed the project might start to exceed its original scope and move into maintaining the extension. This should be defined as business as usual or equipping the extension, which unless in the PID would be a new project.*



## Conclusion

Project management is a way of breaking down the project into defined areas with clear lines of accountability and consultation. Poor project management can lead to a permanent incompletion, rapid escalation of costs and manpower stress and dissatisfaction. GPs might never be in a position to manage a big project, but they might commission, as part of a practice or partnership, large projects such as new builds or extensions, and have financial and executive responsibility for this. This chapter has summarised the processes used by public-sector organisations in the UK, so that GPs will be more aware of the processes around them if called to be part of a team.

## Questions

**1** ▷ What is PRINCE 2?

**2** ▷ Why do projects fail?

3 ▷ What are the key components of a good business case?

4 ▷ What is the scope of a project?

5 ▷ What is a PID?

6 ▷ What are the roles of the project board members?

7 ▷ What does the project manager do?

8 ▷ What levels of planning should there be in a project plan?

9 ▷ What is a Gantt chart?

10 ▷ How is risk managed and quantified?

## *Further reading*

Field M, Keller L. *Project Management* London: Thomson Learning, 2000.

Martin V. *Managing Projects in Health and Social Care* London: Routledge, 2002.

Roberts K, Ludvigsen C. *Project Management for Heath Care Professionals* Oxford: Butterworth-Heinemann, 1998.



### References

1 • Young T. *30 Minutes to Plan a Project* London: Kogan Page, 1997.

2 • Newton R. *The Project Manager: mastering the art of delivery* London: Financial Times and Prentice Hall, 2005.

3 • Office of Government Commerce. *Managing Successful Projects with PRINCE2* (fifth edn) London: The Stationery Office, 2005.

4 • Project Management Institute. *The Practice Standard for Work Breakdown Structures* (second edn) Newtown Square, PA: PMI, 2006.

# Index


Academy of Royal Medical Colleges 157
ACAS *see* Advisory, Conciliation and Arbitration Service
access to health care 9
Access to Health Records Act 113
accountability 39–40, 47
accountants 79, 84–5, 93
accountants' report 98
accounts
  locum GPs 81–3, 96
    annual 84
  notes 90
  partners 88–90, 103–6
  practice 97, 99–102
Acute Hospitals Trust 70
additional services 10
  practice as provider 27
administration and time management 167
administrative staff 74, 75–6
adopters, late/early 189
Advisory, Conciliation and Arbitration Service (ACAS)
  eManager tool 121
  on employment legislation 114
Agenda for Change 110–11
Alternative Provider Medical Services (APMS) 11, 27–8
apathy/non-compliance with change 188
apothecaries 3
appraisal systems 49–51
  as contractual requirement 50
  documentation 51
  *Good Medical Practice* 50
  importance 120
  salaried doctors 65
assistant practice manager 74–5
audit
  audit cycles 43
  in PHCT meetings 77
  role of 42

balance sheets 89
Belbin team roles 130, 133
benefits advisers 72
British Medical Association (BMA) Medical Reform Committee 3
building premises 203–4, 213
  business case 208
  communication plan 211
  cutting project short 219
  exception plan 211
  funding
    current 204
    historical 203–4
  managing/controlling project 216–18
  project board 207
  project manager 207
  project plan 210–12
  project stages 216
  reporting 217–18
  setting up project 206–7
  sign-off 219
  specialist team managers 207–8
  stage plan 210
  team plan 210–11
  tolerances 216–17
  work-/product-breakdown structure 211–12
burnout 167
business case 193–201
  commissioners, submission to 194, 200
  contents 193–4
    evaluation 199–200
      risk assessment 199–200
      success factors 199
      typical case, path of 200
    how much 196–8
      cost/benefit exercise 196–7
    what 194–5
    who/when 195–6
    why 194
  description 193
  development/approval 200
  implementation 200
  marketing 198, 200
  peer reviews 198
  project management 206, 208

set pro forma 199
specificity 193–4
training 200

Caldicott Guardians 46, 63
Caldicott report 63
capital accounts, partners' 89–90
centralisation 15–16
chairing meetings 143–6
choice of chair 143
handling 'problem' delegates 146
roles of chair 144–5
change agents 189, 190
change management 183–92
analysing situation 185–6
evidence 185–9
and Evidence-Based Practice 184
in individuals/organisations 189
large-scale change 190
Lewin's 'equilibrium' 186
Lewin's force field model 186
Lewin's stages of change 185
planning change 186–9
project management 218
readiness–capability assessment 187
Senge's positions of commitment/ enrolment/compliance 188
'whole systems thinking' 190
child protection 61, 62, 71
Citizens Advice Bureaux 73
cleaning staff 76
clinical audit *see* audit
clinical governance 39–42
description/features 40
'leads' 43, 54
in practice 42–8
accountability 47
communication 44
complaints 45
culture 43–4
Evidence-Based Practice 44
leadership 47–8
patient involvement 44
Practice Development Plans (PDPs) 44–5
record-keeping 46
Significant Event Audits 46
teamwork 45–6
primary healthcare team 76–8
seven pillars 41–2
Clinical Governance Support Team 42
clinical leadership *see* leadership, clinical
clinical management 152–3
Collings report 5–6
commissioning/contracting 23–37
commissioning cycle 25
competitive tendering 33
definitions 24–6
evidence 33–4
future 35
and general practice 26
local *vs* population needs 17–18
PCTs 33–4
policy context 23–4
population base 31
practice as commissioner 28–32
practice as provider 26–7
additional services 27
enhanced services 27–8
essential (core) services 27
price negotiation 31
*see also* Local Commissioning Groups; Practice-Based Commissioning; purchaser–providers
commitment to change 188
communication 44
communication plan 211
Community Health Partnerships 18
community matrons 69–70
community midwives 70
complaints 45
compliance with change 188
consultations, UK statistics of 2
Continuing Personal Development (CPD) 51–2
in business case for new service 195
nursing staff 67
and taxation 82
continuity of care 1
contract, new *see* General Medical Services, GMS2 contract (2003)
contracting *see* commissioning/ contracting
contracts of employment, staff 109, 110–12
Controlled Drugs Register 68
core (essential) services 9–10
corporate governance 47
cost reduction initiatives 115
cost rent 203

counselling underperforming staff 117–19
CPD *see* Continuing Personal Development
Critical Event Reviews/Analyses *see* Significant Event Audits
'critical path' scheduling 213
culture of clinical governance 43–4
cycle of change 190

Data Protection Act (1998) 113
delegation 165–8
 accepting tasks 165
 failure to delegate 166
 guidelines 166
 and responsibility 165
 and training 166
demotivation *see* motivation, lack of
Department of Health, Social Services and Public Safety (DHSSPS) 19
dermatology outpatient costs 196–7
diary coding 65
*Diffusion of Innovations* 189
Direct Enhanced Services (DES) 11, 110
Disability Discrimination Act (2005) 113–14
Disability Rights Commission 114
disciplinary procedures 118–19, 179
discrimination 109
dismissal of staff 109, 120–1
dispensing income 88, 100
dispensing staff 75
dissatisfaction and satisfaction 173–4
district nurses 61, 71–2
District Nursing Service 69
Doctor's Educational Needs (DENs) 45
doctors
 partners 60, 62–3
 salaried 60, 63–5
  accountability 65
  job plans 63, 64
  workload 64–5
 specialty registrars/Foundation Yr 2 60, 65–6
drawings policy 92–4
 taxation 93–4
duty patients 65
dying at home 61, 62

education/training
 and delegation 166
 importance 119–20
 post-registration training 6
 postgraduate 7
 QoF requirements 110
 specialty registrars/Foundation Yr 2 doctors 65–6
 vocational training 6
elderly patients 71
elective care 33
eManager tool 121
emergency patients 65
employed staff 66–9
employer, practice as 107–22
Employers' Liability Compulsory Insurance 112
employment of staff 108–10
 contracts 109, 110–12
 discrimination 109
 holiday entitlement 108
 legal requirements 108, 109–10
 legislation/regulation 112–14
 NHS terms/conditions 109
 performance management 114–21
  dismissal of staff 120–1
  legal problems 119–20
  resources, use of
   information system management 115
   new initiatives 115
   non-staff costs 115
   staff time 114
  sickness absence 119
  staff monitoring 115–21
  standards, setting/reviewing 116
   use of protocols 116–17
  underperforming staff
   counselling 117–19
   steps taken 118–19
 rates of pay 111
Employment Rights Act (1996) 121–2
enhanced services 11
 in income/expenditure account 99–100
 practice as provider 27–8
enrolment in change 188
essential (core) services 9–10
 practice as provider 27
Evidence-Based Practice
 and change management theory 184
 clinical governance 44
 initial steps 184

exception plan 211
expectancy theory 176–7
  Lawler–Porter diagram 176
expenditure records
  Continuing Personal Development 82
  locum GPs 81–3
  motoring expenses 82
  partners 88–9
  subscriptions 82
expenses 87–8

Family Practitioner Committees 7
financial issues
  accountants' report 98
  cashflow 92
  locum GPs 80–4, 96–7
  partners 85–94, 97
  practice accounts
    annual financial statement 97
    income/expenditure account 99–102
    partners' accounts 103–6
fire regulations 113
*A First Class Service* 49
Foundation Yr 2 doctors 60, 65–6
fundholding 7

Gantt chart of scheduling 214
General Medical Council (GMC)
  establishment 3
  registration 1
General Medical Services 7–8
  GMS2 contract (2003) 7, 9–11, 15, 26–7, 109
    additional services 10
    enhanced services 11
    essential (core) services 9–10
  income schedule 88
General Practice Fundholders (GPFs) 24
general practices
  as commissioners 28–32
  GMS contract (1990) 7
  group practices 6
  interface with NHS 15–21
  PMS contract 8
  as providers 27–8
  single-handed practices 4
general practitioners (GPs)
  as gatekeepers 5
  health system implications 20
  as leaders *see under* leadership
  as locums 80–4
  newly qualified 153–4
  as partners 85–90
  as principals/business partners 107–8
  as a profession 5
  relationship with district nurses 72
  roles 20
  running a business 79–106
  with a Special Interest (GPwSI) 195
General Practitioners Committee (GPC) Model Contract (2007) 64
*Going Lean in the NHS* 167
*Good Doctors, Safer Patients* 52
Good Medical Practice on appraisals 50
'GP Charter' 6
GPs *see* general practitioners
Griffiths report 6

Health and Safety at Work Act (1974) 112–13
Health and Social Care Department 18–19
Health Service and Public Health Act (1968) 6
health visitors 6, 61, 70–1
healthcare assistants (HCAs) 68–9
  role of 67, 69
healthcare organisations, structure of 151
Herzberg's theory of motivation 173, 174–5, 177
'hierarchy of needs' 135, 172
history of general practice 1–14
  ancient Egyptian/Greek 2–3
  British 3
    20th century 4–12
    General Medical Services 7–8
    Personal Medical Services 8–9
HM Revenue and Customs 80, 84
  online tax/national insurance 92
holiday entitlement 108
human needs 133, 135
'hygiene factors' 174–5

income and expenditure (profit and loss) account 89
income records
  locum GPs 81
  partners 88
infection control 76
infirmaries 3

Information Commissioner's Office 113
information system management 115
innovation 77
innovators 189
integrated care 8
integrated governance 47
interdisciplinary healthcare teams 126
internal market 7, 8

job plan preparation 64–5

laggards 189
Lawler–Porter diagram of expectancy theory 176
leadership 47–8, 125, 154
  behaviours 156
  clinical 152–3
  as collective task 157
  definitions 154–5
  development in future 157–8
  domains/competences 156–7
  in general practice 154–5, 156–7
  GP as leader 151–9
  and management 152–3, 154
  newly qualified GPs 153–4
  shared *vs* distributed 155
  teams 132, 136
leads 195
learning needs 44–5
  specialty registrars/Foundation Yr 2 doctors 65–6
legal problems 119–20
Lewin's 'equilibrium' 186
Lewin's force field model 186
Lewin's stages of change 185
licensing of doctors 50
Limited Liability Partnership Act (2000) 63
Local Commissioning Groups (LCGs) 19
Local Enhanced Services (LES) 11, 99–100
  income generation 110
Local Health Boards (LHBs) 18–19
Local Improvement Finance Trusts (LIFT) 204
Local Medical Committee (LMC) 65
locum GPs' finances 80–4
  income/expenditure accounts 81–3
    Continuing Personal Development 82
    example 96–7
    motoring expenses 82, 96
    subscriptions 82, 96
  superannuation 83
  taxation 81

management and leadership 152–3, 154
Management Team Wheel 131
managerial staff 74
Maslow's 'hierarchy of needs' 135, 172
maternity leave/pay 109
Medical Act (1858) 3
Medical Act (1886) 3
Medical Leadership Competency Framework 157–8
medical secretaries 75
medicine, purpose of 1–2
meetings 77–8
  agenda 142
  avoiding overload 147–8
  chairing 143–5
    control 144
    fairness/creativity/confidentiality 145
    focus 144
    house-keeping 145
    order/clarity 145
    putting delegates at ease 144
  following through 146–7
  frequency 140
  justifying 139–40
  membership 140–1
  minutes 147
  number of delegates 140
  organising/running 139–49
  preparation 142–3
  'problem delegates' 146
  return for attendance 148
  rivalries 146
  roles within 143–4
  subgroups 140
  team bonding 141
  temporary delegates 140
  timing/venue 141–2
  tips for success 148
  *vs* teams 126
midwives 61
  community 70
Modernising Medical Careers 12
motivation
  'carrots' and 'sticks' 174–6, 180
  description 172

expectancy theory 176–7
Lawler–Porter diagram 176
Herzberg's theory of 173, 174–5, 177
'hygiene factors' 174–5
individuals 135
motivating 171–82
tailored to 172
intrinsic *vs* extrinsic 174
lack of 178–82
diagnosis 180–1
management 181–2
symptoms/history 178–80
team-member's point of view 179–80
and meetings 144, 146
models 135
motivators 174–6
repetition of 175–6
satisfaction and dissatisfaction 173–4
and teamwork 126, 129, 133
multidisciplinary 125

National Clinical Assessment Service (NCAS) 53–4
National Enhanced Services (NES) 99
National Health Insurance Act (1919) 4
National Health Service Act (1977) 11
National Health Service (NHS) 4–5
National Institute of Health and Clinical Excellence (NICE) 190
National Insurance (NI) 80
National Patient Safety Authority (NPSA) 48–9
fishbone diagram 49
National Service Frameworks 190
*The New NHS: modern, dependable* 7–8
'New Public Management' 7
NHS *see* National Health Service
NHS and Community Care Act (1990) 7
NHS boards 18
*NHS Improvement Plan* 28, 69–70
NHS Institute for Innovation and Improvement 157–8
NHS Local Improvement Finance Trusts (LIFT) 204
non-NHS staff 60
Northern Ireland primary care 19
notional rent 203–4
nurse practitioners 67–8
Nursing and Midwifery Council on professional responsibilities of nurses 66–7
nursing staff 66–72
practice-based 66, 69–72
practice-employed 66–9, 72
professional responsibilities 66–7
role of 72–3
nursing team lead 67

occupational therapists 73
openness 47
opinion leaders 189
*An Organisation with a Memory* 48

palliative care 62
partners 60, 62–3
financial issues 85–90, 103–6
income 107
responsibilities 108, 113
partnership finances 84
accounts 88–90, 103–6
balance sheets 89
capital accounts 89–90
income/expenditure 88–9
notes 90
financial statement example 97
management 92–4
drawings policy 86, 92–4
superannuation 94
tax liabilities 94
partnership agreement 85–6
patient involvement in clinical governance 44
*Patient Safety* 48
Patient's Unmet Needs (PUNs) 45
PBC *see* Practice-Based Commissioning
PEP eKit 45
performance management 39–57, 114–21
dismissal of staff 120–1
legal problems 119–20
poor performance, reporting 54–5
resources, use of
information system management 115
new initiatives 115
non-staff costs 115
staff time 114
sickness absence 119
staff, monitoring of 115–21
dismissal of staff 120–1

legal problems 119–20
sickness absence 119
standards, setting/reviewing 116
use of protocols 116–17
underperforming staff
counselling 117–19
steps taken 118–19
standards, setting/reviewing 116
use of protocols 116–17
underperforming staff
counselling 117–19
steps taken 118–19
Performance Panel 54
Personal Development Plans (PDPs) 42, 44
Personal Medical Services 8–9
contracts 26–7, 28, 64
income schedule 88
PHCT *see* primary healthcare team
phlebotomists 69
physiotherapists 73
Plan–Do–Study–Act audit cycle 42, 43
podiatrists 73
poor performance, reporting 54–5
Poorly Performing Doctors Panel 54
Postgraduate Education Allowance (PGEA) 7
Postgraduate Medical Education and Training Board (PMETB) competency framework 158
*Practice and Primary Care Management* 110
practice as employer 107–22
Practice-Based Commissioning (PBC) 12, 15, 29–32
aims 29
board 200
budgets 30
conflicts of interest 32–3
avoidance/management 34
definitions 29
early stages 28
establishment 24
'good practice' compendium 30
PCT support 31
and primary healthcare team 61
responsibilities/requirements 30–2
service redesign 30
Practice Development Plans (PDPs) 44–5
practice finances 107
accounts
annual financial statement 97
income/expenditure account 99–102
partners' accounts 103–6
expenditures 108
income generation 107–8
staff costs 108
practice manager 74
practice nurses 6, 68
senior 67
Practitioner with a Special Interest 194
primary care
management framework 16
Northern Ireland 19
proportion of NHS 16
Scotland 18
Wales 18–19
Primary Care Clinical Governance Team 42
primary care development consultants 204
Primary Care Groups (PCGs) 16
Primary Care Trust Medical Services (PCTMS) 11
Primary Care Trusts/Organisations (PCTs/PCOs)
clinical governance leads 54
commissioning/contracting 27, 33–4
legal responsibility 31
local *vs* population needs 17–18
establishment 16–20
functions 16–17
and GMS2 contract 9
monitoring 17
numbers 17
and performance management 54
Performance Panel 54
PMS contract 8–9
Professional Executive Committee 33
*Primary Health Care: an agenda for discussion* 6
primary healthcare team (PHCT) 59–79
assistant practice manager 74–5
and clinical governance 76–8
clinical staff, other 60
district nurses 61
doctors
partners 60, 62–3
salaried 60, 63–5
specialty registrars/Foundation Yr 2 60, 65–6
effects of PBC 61

employed staff 66–9
health visitors 61
managerial/administrative staff 74
meetings 77–8
midwives 61
non-NHS staff 60
nursing staff 66–72
practice-based 69–72
practice-employed 66–9
role of 72–3
occupational therapists 73
physiotherapists 73
podiatrists 73
practice-employed *vs* -based staff 59–61, 66
practice manager 74
role of 61–2
social workers/advisers 73
PRINCE 205
Private Finance Initiatives (PFIs) 204
probity 47
problem people 132–6
product breakdown structure 211–12
productivity issues 167–8
profit and loss (income and expenditure) account 89
project management 203–20
building premises 203–4
business case 208
change management 218
checkpoint reports 217
closing project 218–19
communication plan 211
controls 216
cutting project short 219
definitions 204–5
end of stage reports 217
estimating 212–13
evaluation
at project end 219
risk 215
exception plan 211
exception reports 217
highlight reports 217
managing/controlling project 216–18
methodology 205–6
project board 207
project end reports 218
project failure 205–6
project manager 207
project plan 210
levels 210–12
project stages 216
reactive/adaptive methods 205
reporting 217–18
risk 213–15
evaluation 215
identification 213
management/analysis cycle 213
monitor/report 215
register 215
response 215
scheduling 213
Gantt chart 214
setting up project 206–7
business case 206
Project Initiation Document 206–7
project team 207
scope 206
sign-off 219
SMART mnemonic 206, 208–9
specialist team managers 207–8
stage plan 210
support 208
team plan 210
tolerances 216–17
work-/product-breakdown structure 211–12
project plan 210
levels 210–12
PRojects IN Controlled Environments (PRINCE) 205
*Promoting Better Health* 7
purchaser–providers
advantages 32
conflicts of interest 32–3
avoidance/management 34
separation 7, 19, 20
purpose of medicine 1–2

QoF *see* Quality and Outcomes Framework
quality
variation in health organisations
*see also* clinical governance
Quality and Outcomes Framework (QoF)
discussion in PHCT meetings 77
employment of staff 110
and GMS2 contract 9, 110
original/updated domains 10

standards for clinical/non-clinical work 62
*Quality in General Practice* policy statement 6

receptionists 75
recertification of GPs 52, 53
record keeping 46
protection of information 113
staff records 120
redundancy 121–2
Regulatory Reform (Fire Safety) Order 2005 113
relicensure of GPs 52
*Report of the Review of Patient-Identifiable Information* 63
reporting poor performance 54–5
revalidation of GPs 52–3
Royal College of General Practitioners (RCGP)
on audits 42
on clinical supervision 66
on CPD 51
first council meeting 4
foundation 5–6
membership 1
examinations 12
*Patient Safety* 48
PEP eKit 45
*Quality in General Practice* policy statement 6
resources for registrars 65
on team-building 125

*Safeguarding Patients* 52
satisfaction and dissatisfaction 173–4
Scotland, primary care in 18
secretaries, medical 75
self-employment 80
service development
business case for 193–201
cost/risk assessments 196
costs 197
non-financial 197–8
service redesign 30, 147
*Seven Steps to Patient Safety* 48–9
*Shifting the Balance of Power within the NHS* 16
sickness absence 119
Significant Event Audits 46
SMART mnemonic 206, 208–9
social workers 73
specialty registrars 60, 65–6
staff
abuse of goodwill 116
disciplinary procedures 118–19
dismissal 120–1
appeal meeting 120
informal counselling 118
legal problems 119–20
management 116
monitoring of 115–21
records 120
redundancy 121
sickness absence 119
standards, setting/reviewing 116
use of protocols 116–17
time, use of 114
underperforming
counselling 117–19
steps taken 118–19
stage plan 210
Statutory Maternity Leave/Pay 109
STOP mnemonic 163
Strategic Health Authorities (SHAs)
creation 16
roles 16, 17
Strategic Service Development Plans 204
superannuation
locum GPs 83
partners 86–7, 94
*Supporting Doctors, Protecting Patients* 49, 53
surgeons, history of 3
SWOT analysis 186

taxation 90–2
and drawings 93–4
locum GPs 80, 81
responsibilities 92
tax calculation 91–2
tax liabilities 94
tax payments 90–1
tax returns 90
team plan 210–11
teamwork/teams 45–6
authority rule 129
bonding in meetings 140
consensus 129
culture 43–4
decision-making 129–30

definitions of team 124–5, 126
development 128–9, 131–2
and difficult team members 134
phases 128
difficult team members 132–6
motivation/needs 135
organisational context 134
reasons for difficulties 132–3
taking action 135–6
team development issues 134
effective management 127–31
effective team players 132
exploring differences 133
and human needs 133
leadership 125, 132, 136
maintaining team 131–2
majority/minority rule 129
meetings *vs* teams 126
motivation/development 123–38
process issues 127
'psychological safety' 131
requirement for team 127
research on 125–6, 131
nature of teams 126
NHS context 125
self-awareness 126, 131
task issues 127
team-building training programmes 125
team roles 130–1
Belbin 130, 133
Management Team Wheel 131
team *vs* organisation 124–5
unanimity 130
*see also* primary healthcare team
time management 161–70
benefits 162
delaying actions 168–9
and delegation 165–8
accepting tasks 165
failure to delegate 166
description 162
poor, and productivity issues 167–8
prioritisation 164–5
time wasting 168
'to-do lists' 162–4
example 163–4
typical 163
urgency/importance 164–5
*Tomorrow's Doctors* 158
Total Purchasing Pilots 28
training *see* education/training
transparency 47
transtheoretical model of the cycle of change 190
triage patients 65
*Trust, Assurance and Safety* 52

vaccine costs 115
Vocational Training Act (1977) 6

Wales, primary care in 18–19
websites
audits 42
Caldicott Guardians 46, 63
clinical governance resources 42
clinical supervision 66
commissioning/contracting 35
on CPD 51
employment legislation 109, 114
on good practice 194
job plan preparation 64
protection of information 113
taxation 80
Working in Partnership Programme 69
'whistle-blowers' 53
work breakdown structure 211–12
Working in Partnership Programme 69
*Working for Patients* 6
workload demands 161–2